HIGHER

SUCCESS WITH BEC

THE NEW BUSINESS ENGLISH CERTIFICATES COURSE

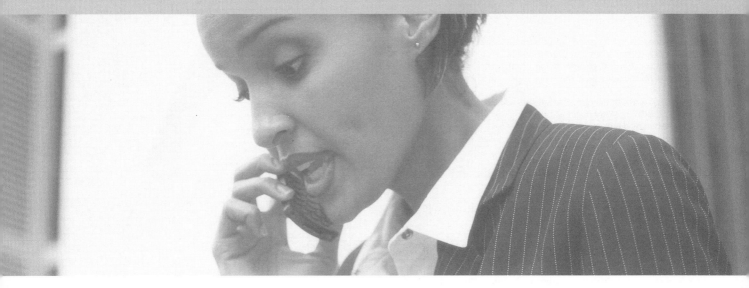

WORKBOOK

PAUL DUMMETT

Summertown
Publishing

Published by:
Summertown Publishing Ltd.,
Aristotle House
Aristotle Lane
Oxford
OX2 6TR
United Kingdom

www.summertown.co.uk
email: info@summertown.co.uk

Workbook without key edition 978 1 902741 96 3
Workbook with key edition 978 1 905992 05 8

© Summertown Publishing Limited 2008
First published 2008

Page design and setting: Oxford Designers & Illustrators
Illustrated by Gary Wing pages 28, 51.
Cover design by white space
© Summertown Publishing Limited 2008

Acknowledgements
The author would like to thank David Riley for 'making a proper writer of me'.

The publishers would like to dedicate the Success with BEC series to the memory of its inspirational editor, David Riley.

The publishers would like to thank and acknowledge the following sources for diagrams, copyright material and trademarks:

Learning to Love the Bloggers – copyright Guardian News & Media 2007.
The 7 Myths of Selling – extract reproduced with permission of Kelley Robertson.
Kelley Robertson, author of *The Secrets of Power Selling* helps sales professionals improve their results. Receive a FREE copy of *100 Ways to Increase Your Sales* by subscribing to his free newsletter available at www.kelleyrobertson.com. Kelley conducts workshops and speaks regularly at sales meetings and conferences. For information on his programs contact him at 905 633 7750 or Kelley@ RobertsonTrainingGroup.com.
Page 26 – chart of data – data sourced from the Central Intelligence Agency.
Eight winning tips to make your financial plan profitable – based on article *Don't wait for tax time to look at the bottom line* by C.J Hayden. www.getclientsnow.com/feb2003.htm.
What sort of boss really cares about his staff? – based on article *What sort of boss gives a monkey's about staff?* by Simon Caulkin – copyright Guardian News & Media Ltd 2007.
Business Life: *Uncomfortable truths about the work life balance* – reproduced with permission of Financial Times.
Halt all this mindless waste of energy – based on letter by P. Dubois-Pèlerin.
Corporate social responsibility – Coca-Cola HBC Press Release for announcing 2006 CSR Report – ©Coca Cola HBC.
Negotiating – based on article *Negotiating skills – what's my interest?* – published in Ezine Articles.com – written by Kevin Dwyer of www.changefactory.com.au.
Bosch warns on innovation risk-aversion – based on article by Richard Milne & Oliver Wihofszki – reproduced with the permission of Financial Times.
Proud of his Prius – reproduced from *Proud of his Prius* by Jeremy Skidmore – published in The Times. © NI Syndication, London (13 April 2007).
The £7 billion pound woman by Jeremy Skidmore – published in The Times. © NI Syndication, London (30 January 2007).

Summertown Publishing would also like to acknowledge the *Business English Certificates Handbook* (published by University of Cambridge ESOL Examinations) as the source of exam formats and rubrics in the Exam Spotlight lessons and other exam-type activities throughout the book.

Photography
Getty Images cover. Honda Motor Company page 5. Getty Images pages 11, 17, 20, 25, 30, 32, 35, 40, 42, 45, 50. PA Photos page 55. Getty Images pages 57, 62.

Printed in Malta

CONTENTS

1.1 Working life

Describing working life

I Put the correct word into each gap to complete this biography of Soichiro Honda, the founder of the Honda Motor Company.

set up   ~~founded~~   worked   joined   applied
retired   moved   left   recruited
graduated   trained   educated

Soichiro Honda, the man who **(0)** *founded* the Honda motor company, has been described as a maverick in a nation of conformists. He was born in 1906 and was **(1)** _____ only

to elementary level. He **(2)** _____ home in his teens to find his fortune in Tokyo. In 1922 he **(3)** _____ for a job in an auto-repair shop. They hired him and **(4)** _____ him to be an auto-mechanic. In his spare time he built his own racing car from handmade parts and an old aircraft engine.

In 1937 he **(5)** _____ his own company, making piston rings, but quickly he realised that he lacked knowledge of making alloy metals. So he **(6)** _____ a technical school so that he could apply what he learnt in his own factory. He never formally **(7)** _____ from the school because he did not bother to take the final examination. He said that a diploma was 'worth less than a movie theatre ticket. A ticket guarantees that you can get into the theatre. But a diploma doesn't guarantee that you can make a living.'

In 1948 Honda Motor began manufacturing small motorcycles. These were dismissed by the dominant American and British manufacturers of the time, but in reality the inexpensive imports brought new people to motorcycling and changed the industry forever.

Soichiro Honda was an inventor at heart who often **(8)** _____ alongside his workers on the floor of his factories. In 1950 he **(9)** _____ business executive Takeo Fujisawa to manage the company so that he could focus on engineering problems.

In 1973, Honda, at 67, **(10)** _____ on the 25th anniversary of the founding of the company. But he asked that it should remain a youthful company. 'Honda has always **(11)** _____ ahead of the times, and I attribute its success to the fact that the firm possesses dreams and youthfulness,' Honda said at the time.

2 Put each word in the correct form to complete the sentence.

0 Students wishing to be considered for a grant must fill out the D17 *application* form.   APPLY

1 I was extremely lucky to find a job; the _____ rate in our area is about 20%.   EMPLOY

2 We got a lot of attention: on the course I attended there were only two _____ to every one trainer.   TRAIN

3 Our _____ policy doesn't allow us to employ people without a university degree.   RECRUIT

4 I'm much more interested in job satisfaction than the level of my _____ .   PAY

5 I've just got a _____ to department manager, but in fact my responsibilities are the same as before.   PROMOTE

6 We received over 500 _____ for just 15 vacancies.   APPLY

7 She's not very happy in her _____ ; she'd prefer to be working still.   RETIRE

8 I'll be out of the office all next week; I'm on a sales _____ course.   TRAIN

Gerund and infinitive

3 Group the words and phrases with a similar meaning.

> I plan   There's no point   I am prepared
> It's useless   I am considering   I adore
> I'm keen on   I am thinking of   I wasn't able
> I aim   I am happy   I failed

1 a It's not worth
   b _____ } + gerund
   c _____

2 a I intend
   b _____ } + infinitive
   c _____

3 a I am thinking about
   b _____ } + gerund
   c _____

4 a I am willing
   b _____ } + infinitive
   c _____

5 a I enjoy
   b _____ } + gerund
   c _____

6 a I didn't manage
   b _____ } + infinitive
   c _____

4 Rewrite each sentence using a gerund or infinitive phrase.

0 Peter thinks golf is a great way to relax.
Peter enjoys *playing golf*.

1 It's very strange for me to drive on the left.
I'm not used to _____ .

2 Her main strength is management of people.
She is good at _____ .

3 I am definitely going to leave at the end of the year.
I plan _____ .

4 Did you have any luck contacting Jane?
Did you manage _____ ?

5 She thinks that increasing the prices is a mistake.
She is reluctant _____ .

6 Were there any problems with software download?
Did you have any difficulty _____ ?

7 Will I have to speak in French?
Does the job involve _____ ?

8 Can you tell me your approximate time of arrival?
When do you expect _____ ?

9 We could go to the cinema tonight, if you like?
What do you think about _____ ?

10 Don't call me between 10 and 12.
Please avoid _____ .

11 The flights are all full. How about the train?
The flights are full. Would you consider _____ ?

12 I don't need to fly business class on such a short journey.
It's not worth _____ .

Pronunciation

5 Look at where stress falls in the following words. What rules can you make?

reti**re** dism**iss** **bu**siness **kno**wledge **pros**pects
empl**oy** recr**uit** **of**fice **for**tune ap**ply**

6 Mark where the stress falls in each of these words.

background supply contract student promote
involve retain college attend status

7 Each of these words can be a noun OR a verb. Decide which each one is according to where the stress is marked.

pre**sent** per**mit** **ob**ject in**crease**
conflict **con**test ex**port** in**sult**

Reading

8 Which of these job advertisements:

0 is aimed at people fresh from university? A
1 requires the candidate to be self-motivated? ____
2 is part of an equal opportunities scheme? ____
3 asks for proof of the candidate's honesty and suitability? ____
4 demands a high level of qualifications? ____
5 doesn't require the candidate to have worked in that field before? ____
6 is to join a young, fast-growing company? ____
7 offers the chance of promotion? ____

A

Trainee Consultants

We are looking for bright and capable young graduates to join our highly successful business consulting team. No direct experience is necessary as training will be given but candidates must show an understanding of the business environment and a willingness to learn. Excellent career prospects. Apply in writing to PO Box 34.

B

Senior health coordinator

Lancashire Health Authority invites independent and responsible candidates with a masters degree in nursing, ten years' nursing experience and at least three years' management experience to apply for this challenging post. Lancashire Authority will consider each application on its own merits, regardless of the candidate's sex, religion or ethnic background.

C

Web designers

Sparking Solutions was voted 'most dynamic newcomer' by IT World magazine two years ago. Our reputation is built on our ability to provide innovative, creative and fun solutions in the world of online marketing. Sounds like you?
Apply to gemma@brightandsparking.com
Please supply character references.

1.2 Asking and answering questions

Indirect questions

1 Read the interview between a journalist and the chairman of an energy company, following a 15% rise in prices to its electricity customers. Put the sentences in the right order.

1 First of all, Dr Wolf, can you tell me why this price rise is necessary?

2 Obviously, it's not something we wanted to do. It has been forced on us by higher oil prices.

_____ I can't speak for others but I would be surprised if they didn't increase them in the near future.

_____ And finally, do you know why other companies haven't increased their prices by the same amount?

_____ These new prices are necessary to protect our future profits, not our past profits.

_____ But you don't actually produce much of your electricity from burning oil, do you?

_____ But even if gas has gone up, how can you justify these prices when you have just announced record profits?

_____ Oh, I see. So you'll be making just as much money out of your customers this year, will you?

_____ In fact, our profits this year will be used to fund a very expensive investment programme in our network.

_____ No, but the price of gas is linked to the price of oil and we do burn lot of gas.

2 Convert these questions into direct questions.

0 Can you tell me why this price rise is necessary?
  Why is this price rise necessary?

1 But you don't actually produce much of your electricity from burning oil, do you?

_____

_____

2 So you'll be making just as much money out of your customers this year, will you?

_____

_____

3 Do you know why other companies haven't increased their prices by the same amount?

_____

_____

3 Put the words into the correct order to make questions.

0 how / far / is / you / know / do / the station
  Do you know how far the station is?

1 quite / you / aren't / inexperienced / are / you

_____

_____ ?

2 sales experience / how / have / do / much / you

_____

_____ ?

3 you / think / you / for the job / have / do / the necessary skills

_____

_____ ?

4 you / have / have / done / you / before / this kind of work

_____

_____ ?

5 like / a coffee / you / would

_____

_____ ?

6 don't / in London / you / live / you / do

_____

_____ ?

7 why / leave / last job / you / your / did

_____

_____ ?

8 why / you / tell / me / you / this job / can / attractive / find

_____

_____ ?

The following article, taken from *Management Now* magazine, is about young people's attitudes to work. Give yourself about twelve minutes to do this reading test.

- Look at the sentences below and read the comments by five managers on the attitudes of young workers to their jobs.
- Match each statement (1–7) to one of the extracts (A, B, C, D or E).
- You will need to use some of the letters more than once.

0 The education system does not prepare young people for working life. D

1 It is the older generation who must accept that attitudes have changed. _____

2 Young people's free time is very important to them. _____

3 Young workers are just as dedicated to their jobs as in the past. _____

4 Young people are very concerned about their earning power. _____

5 Employers cannot assume their employees will stay with them for a long time. _____

6 Young people do not have the patience to train and learn at work. _____

7 It suits companies too, if employees come and go. _____

A

I find that the priorities of young employees are very different to my generation and previous generations. Leisure time is now much more organised than it was 20 years ago. When my parents had a break from work they used to do very little other than just relax. Nowadays, people want to plan an activity holiday or an action-packed weekend – to go diving or climbing or whitewater rafting. So necessarily they spend more time thinking about and planning these leisure events. This naturally has a knock-on effect on their work – they think less about work and more about leisure time.

B

Young workers certainly feel less commitment to their employers than in the past. But in many ways employers have themselves to blame for this. The demands on companies to be more competitive means that they hire people and then lay them off pretty much as they please. They need this flexibility. In other words, they don't show much loyalty to their own staff. What we are seeing now is a reaction to this. Employees have much less loyalty to their employers these days. If you ask a young person how many jobs he expects to have in his life, he will generally say about five to ten.

C

I think that the work-life balance that young people have found is much healthier than it was in the past. They don't just live for work – they think about what they are working for. At the same time employers have moved to take account of this by offering more flexibility in working hours, better maternity or paternity leave conditions so that young parents can have more time with their children, and so on. It's a natural evolution. Just because young people have more commitment to getting their home life right, it doesn't necessarily follow that they are less committed to their jobs.

D

I worry that standards in our schools and universities have dropped quite dramatically and that people entering the workforce are very poorly equipped to deal with the demands of working life. What is more worrying is that the graduates themselves don't realise this. They think they have all the necessary qualifications and knowledge to be successful at work, when in fact they are lacking. So when they are faced with the prospect of learning more on the job and serving their time to gain this necessary experience, they become frustrated. The fact is that many of them have an over-inflated opinion of their own worth to the company, and they need to be made aware of this.

E

The attitudes of young workers are part of the change in values that we see around us generally. The most significant of these values are: first, a fear of being poor. There are so many images of material wealth around and young people want a part of it. Second, the belief that respect has to be earned – it cannot just be expected by elders or seniors at work. Thirdly, a belief in expressing yourself rather than controlling yourself, which perhaps earlier generations thought was a virtue. So we, the older generation, must accept that these are the values of today and adapt to them in order to get the best from our young workforce.

2.1 Growing the company

Parts of a company

1 Write the word that fits the definition. The first letter has been given.

0 A company which pays a fee to use another company's name and sell its services:

a f ranchise

1 A building where finished goods or raw materials are stored: a w _____

2 A company which is more than 50% owned by another (holding or parent) company:

a s _____

3 A building where manufacturing, assembling or packing activity takes place: a p _____

4 The offices where the top management and administration are based: the h _____

5 A (large) part of a company that has responsibility for one area or activity: a d _____

2 Complete each newspaper headline using a word or phrase from the box.

> expands   sell off   go public   goes bankrupt
> merge   take-over   laid off

British bank fears _____ by cash-rich Spanish giant

Car plant closes: 800 _____

Keltel to _____ failing Internet business

BP and Shell _____ to form world's largest oil company

3 Complete the table.

Verb	Noun
expand	expansion
develop	
merge	
acquire	
grow	
innovate	innovation
	solution
	classification
	evolution
	tendency

Pronunciation

4 Look at where the stress falls in the following words of three syllables or more. What rules can you make about: a) those ending in -*ion* b) the rest?

inno**va**tion   responsi**bi**lity   ex**pan**sion   **ten**dency
pro**duc**tion   so**lu**tion   acqui**si**tion   **com**pany
revenue   ac**ti**vity

5 Mark where the stress falls in each of these words.

bankruptcy   evolution   division   subsidiary
strategy   distribution   significant   competition
competitive   philosophy

Deanly shares will _____ next year

Administrators called in as Lanco _____

Chemico _____ its European operations by buying Toxico

Past tenses

6 Complete the table of irregular verbs.

Present	Past	Past participle
begin		begun
become	became	
lose	lost	
buy		
put		put
rise		risen
fall	fell	
feel		
spend	spent	
find		found
found		

7 Complete this extract from a newspaper article by choosing the best sentence (A–G) for each gap (1–6).

The extraordinary fact about many successful businesses in the UK is that in the last twenty years they have not made their money from what they produce or sell. **(0)** A Take the example of St Coates College. **(1)** ___ It targeted the children of rich Europeans who wanted to send their children to the UK to study for their pre-university qualification. **(2)** ___ Business was good, however, and in the mid-70s the college decided it made more sense to buy houses in the neighbourhood to use as accommodation. **(3)** ___ Over the next fifteen years their value tripled. **(4)** ___ The profits of the business itself, after servicing the property loans, were, by comparison, only moderate. St Coates is not the only business to have made its money in this way. **(5)** ___ But what has been lost along the way? **(6)** ___ Now, meeting the demand for products and services is no longer of the same interest – all a person needs to do is buy a property and sit on it for ten years.

A Rather they have profited from huge rises in the value of property.

B By the early 1990's it had purchased over twenty such properties.

C It was founded in the 1960's as a college for the International Baccalaureate Exam.

D Twenty years ago, before the property boom, people were making things and providing services.

E The same model has been applied in many sectors and places all over the country.

F During its early years it used to rent accommodation to house these students.

G So the assets of the college increased enormously.

8 Some of the following extracts from a transport company's annual report contain mistakes with tenses. If the sentence is correct, mark it with a ✓. If it is wrong, correct it.

0 2007 ~~has been~~ a better year than we had originally anticipated.   *was*

00 At the beginning of the year we <u>won</u> a contract to build a new metro system in Singapore.   ✓

1 Even though revenue was down over the course of the year, our profit margins <u>improved</u>.   _____

2 In April we <u>had begun</u> work on a bus terminal in Shanghai.   _____

3 In Shanghai we used the same design that we <u>used to use</u> in Beijing a year earlier.   _____

4 Because many existing projects <u>were coming</u> to an end, we made it a priority to look for new business.   _____

5 In May, a new head of International Business <u>has been</u> appointed.   _____

6 We found that we <u>wasted</u> a lot of time in the planning stages.   _____

7 The official opening <u>was</u> attended by the President of Iran.   _____

8 Our R & D department <u>was working</u> on a new high speed railway which will be launched next year.   _____

Organisational culture

9 Write in the missing letters to complete the chart.

E _ _ l _ y _ _ s   Customers

Stakeholders

_ h _ _ eh _ _ _ e _ s   S _ _ _ lie _ s

Lo _ a _ com _ _ _ ity

10 Make each noun into an adjective to complete each statement.

0 I feel *secure* in my job.   SECURITY

1 I am very _____ in the development of new products.   INVOLVEMENT

2 Customers are generally very _____ with the service they get.   SATISFACTION

3 We have a very _____ structure, with about fifteen levels from top to bottom.   HIERARCHY

4 It's a very _____ company which empowers individuals.   INNOVATION

5 I am consulted both on everyday matters and also on more _____ decisions.   STRATEGY

11 Make each adjective into a noun to complete each statement.

6 At Google the emphasis is on _____ .   INFORMAL

7 Like most banks our culture is influenced by the amount of _____ .   BUREAUCRATIC

8 The most important thing for employees is to have _____ ; not constant change.   CONSISTENT

9 In advertising, the main thing is to bring out employees' natural _____ .   CREATIVE

10 _____ can be financial or simply a few words of praise.   RECOGNISED

12 Below is a checklist for a healthy work environment. Complete the statements by choosing the best word from the box.

> satisfaction   recognised   ~~values~~   clear   balance   mutual   retention   reward   empowered   welfare

Healthy Workplace Checklist

☐ Senior leadership in my organisation (**0**) *values* employees. (eg takes employees' needs into account when key decisions are being made.)

☐ Workplace health is the responsibility of all leaders (senior leaders down to front-line supervisors) in my organisation.

☐ My organisation walks the talk when it comes to work-life (**1**) _____ . (eg we do not (**2**) _____ employees who work long hours, just those who are productive.)

☐ Employees in my organisation feel (**3**) _____ : they have a great degree of control over how they do their work and are involved in decisions that affect them.

☐ I work in a safe environment where on-the-job accidents are very rare.

☐ Employees in my organisation feel that the work they do is (**4**) _____ and that they get adequate feedback.

☐ I work in a culture of (**5**) _____ trust and respect.

☐ Customer (**6**) _____ is high, but does not come at the expense of employee (**7**) _____ .

☐ There are (**8**) _____ lines of communication (both top-down and bottom-up) in my organisation.

☐ People enjoy coming to work and attendance is very high.

☐ My organisation enjoys high (**9**) _____ because people do not want to leave.

2.2 Presenting facts

1 Match each phrase on the left with the one closest in meaning on the right.

0	Let's get started	A	Feel free to interrupt
1	It's worth noting	B	That brings me to the end
2	the main points	C	To sum up
3	Stop me at any time	D	Shall we begin?
4	Can everyone hear alright?	E	I should mention
5	I digress	F	Getting back to the subject
6	In conclusion	G	I won't take up much of your time
7	I'll finish there	H	Would you like me to speak up?
8	I'll try to be brief	I	the key issues

2 Complete this presentation by writing ONE word in each gap.

OK. (**0**) *Shall* we get started? Today I'd like (**1**) _____ present some information about Cranthorne Ltd, which, (**2**) _____ you know, is a potential takeover target for us. Please interrupt (**3**) _____ something is not clear, but otherwise, I'd ask you to leave your questions (**4**) _____ the end of my presentation. I'd like to begin (**5**) _____ giving you a brief history of the company.

Cranthorne has been (**6**) _____ business for over 40 years but (**7**) _____ recently found trading conditions very tough. There are several reasons for this: first, ...

... and so the current management is keen to find an investor to help them fund their plans.

I think I've covered (**8**) _____ main points. To sum (**9**) _____ , I'd say Cranthorne represents the best investment opportunity we have. Now, if you have any questions, I'll do (**10**) _____ best to answer them.

3 This sentence is grammatically incorrect: 'I'd like to <u>talk you</u> about my experience.' Instead, we can either say 'I'd like to <u>talk about</u> ...' or 'I'd like to <u>talk to you</u> about ...' or 'I'd like to <u>tell you</u> about ...' . Correct the following sentences.

0 I need to talk my manager about that.
   talk *to* my manager

1 I'd like to present you our latest design.
  _____

2 I'm going to describe you the development over the last four years.
  _____

3 And I'd like to ask to you this question: why ...?
  _____

4 Can anyone tell why we should take such a risk?
  _____

5 When I have explained you the reasons, you will understand.
  _____

6 The next graph shows to you how we achieved these results.
  _____

4 Imagine you are going to discuss the points below. Write sentences to present your opinion. Use the phrases in the box to help you.

- Do you think it's better to work for a big organisation or a small company?
- Do you think management of people is something that can be learned, or is it a natural quality?
- What do you think will be the really big growth areas of the economy over the next fifteen years?

Useful language

Personally, I think ...
In my opinion, ...
On the whole, ...
I'm not sure: on the one hand, ... on the other hand ...
You're right.
I agree with you.
Maybe so, but ...
No, I don't see it that way. For me, ...

1 Complete the responses to the examiner's questions using the phrases in the box.

> ~~very much~~   actually   not really   on the whole
> I doubt it   I don't see it that way   for me
> I agree   I might do

0 *Do you like living in Beijing?*
Very much. It's a really exciting city

1 *So, French is your first language?*
_____ , it's German

2 *Is it a well-paid job?*
Yes but, _____ , money is not the most important thing.

3 *Outsourcing does have many advantages.*
_____ . I think it is a very risky strategy.

4 *I believe it's a very competitive sector.*
_____ , that's true, but there are opportunities.

5 *Would you like to work in the public sector?*
_____ . It tends to be less dynamic.

6 *And do you think you will stay in Singapore?*
_____ . It's only a two-year contract.

7 *Choosing the right course is very important.*
_____ . It affects your whole career.

2 What do these examiners' comments mean? Match each comment (1–5) with one of the phrases (A–F).

0 That sounds exciting. I expect you're raring to go.	A If you don't take risks, you won't win anything.
1 Well it's not everyone's cup of tea.	B Good luck.
2 You've obviously done your homework.	C You must be keen to start.
3 Nothing ventured, nothing gained.	D I approve of your decision.
4 Well, I wish you all the best.	E It doesn't suit everybody.
5 I think that's very wise.	F You've researched it carefully.

3 Each of the student's responses below contains two mistakes which are underlined. Correct them.

0 **Examiner** Where are you working at the moment?
Candidate I am working <u>like</u> an apprentice <u>on</u> a pharmaceutical company.
I am working as an apprentice for a …

1 **Examiner** What does your job involve exactly?
Candidate I am responsible <u>of</u> searching the press <u>all days</u> for articles about our company.

2 **Examiner** Will you continue to work there at the end of your apprenticeship?
Candidate Yes, I hope <u>it</u>. But maybe I <u>must</u> apply for a job with another company.

3 **Examiner** And what do you hope to be doing ten years from now?
Candidate My ambition is <u>that I will work</u> in the marketing field, because that is what I <u>am specialised</u> in.

4 **Examiner** Do you think it's OK for pharmaceutical companies to advertise medicines?
Candidate It depends <u>for</u> what kind of product they are advertising. In my <u>vision</u>, it's fine to advertise if you are honest about the benefits.

5 **Examiner** But perhaps that's not always the case?
Candidate I <u>am agree</u> with you that some companies overstate benefits, but <u>in whole</u> they are very responsible.

Means of communication

1 Complete this job advertisement for an assistant press officer by writing the correct verb in each gap.

> ### Assistant press officer wanted
>
> We are seeking a motivated, independent press relations officer to assist our busy team. Candidates should have at least 10 years' experience in the field, preferably with a multinational corporation. The job will involve (0) *making* and (1) _____ calls from members of the press; (2) _____ press releases; (3) _____ public meetings with the Chairman and, where necessary, (4) _____ the minutes; coaching the Chairman before he (5) _____ presentations or speeches; helping to (6) _____ the company's annual report; (7) _____ news about the company's activities on our website; liaising with the marketing department about the (8) _____ of advertising campaigns; keeping department heads informed of new developments by (9) _____ memos to all concerned.

2 Use the clues below to complete this crossword with words related to communication.

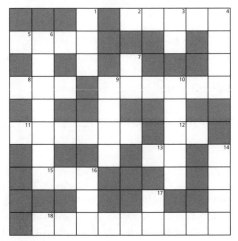

Across

2 and 4 down to suggest different products to a customer who is already buying another product (5, 4)

5, 7 down and 9 down direct contact with someone, not over the phone or by Internet (4, 2, 4)

8 and 12 a short form for a recruiting advertisement (3, 2)

9 and 6 down an official letter or statement saying you are sorry (6, 7)

11 a piece of paper put on a wall or on a website giving official information (6)

12 see 8

13 'let's keep ____ touch' (2)

15 'Sorry. I haven't called her _____' (3)

18 If you would like to thank someone formally, you 'express your ____' (9)

Down

1 the past of 'meet' (3)

3 and 14 When someone is speaking on the telephone they are '___ the _____' (2, 4)

4 see 2 across

6 see 9 across

7 see 5 across

9 see 5 across

10 'a ____ of communication' (5)

16 'a ____ break' can be taken in the morning or afternoon (3)

17 abbreviation for computing or information technology (2)

3 A call centre operator is trying to deal sensitively with a customer complaint. Put in the correct auxiliary verb to complete each statement.

do	'll	would	can	may	do	H̶l̶	would

0 I 'll see what I can do.

1 I _____ apologise for the delay.

2 If you _____ be kind enough to give me your mobile number, I'll call you back in a few minutes.

3 I _____ understand your worries.

4 _____ 9 am be a convenient time?

5 I _____ get back to you as soon as I can.

6 _____ I be of any more assistance?

7 You _____ call me on this number whenever you like.

Pronunciation

4 Native speakers often contract the auxiliaries *have, had, will,* and *would*. Practise saying these phrases.

I'd love to.	I wish I'd known.
I'll call you.	I've met her before.
If I'd had more time, I'd 've visited you.	
She'll 've finished by this afternoon.	

Verb patterns

5 Match each verb on the left with the one closest in meaning on the right.

0 thank	A invite
1 promise	B convince
2 urge	C be grateful
3 suggest	D blame
4 persuade	E discourage
5 dissuade	F encourage
6 ask	G undertake
7 criticise	H propose

6 Each pair of verbs in exercise 5 is followed by the same grammatical form. Write the form that follows each.

0 thank and be grateful (to someone) for something **or** for doing something

1 _____

2 _____

3 _____

4 _____

5 _____

6 _____

7 _____

7 Change each of the direct quotations from newspaper reports into reported statements.

0 'It's entirely the fault of the banks. They should have been more open about their charges to customers,' one industry commentator said.

An industry commentator blamed the banks for not being open about their charges to customers.

1 Asked by business leaders what he would do to help them, the Finance Minister said, 'I will first simplify the tax system and then step by step reduce the burden of tax on companies.'

The Finance Minister promised _____
_____ .

2 The Chairman of Chrysler told investors, 'We must be patient. The current downturn is part of the economic cycle and there will be better times again.'

The Chairman urged _____
_____ .

3 A source close to the management said, 'It's a really good product, but the world isn't ready for it yet. They should relaunch it in a year or so.'

A source close to the management suggested ___
_____ .

4 Hamilton had these words for his team. 'Everyone has worked very hard and unselfishly to achieve this success.'

Hamilton praised _____
_____ .

5 Fredericks defended the appointment of his son, saying, 'There is no favouritism here; Nigel has got the job purely on merit.'

Fredericks denied _____
_____ .

6 The industry watchdog was less complimentary. 'Degas have put unfair pressure on customers to sign up to new contracts – they haven't broken the rules, but they have bent them!'

The industry watchdog criticised _____
_____ .

7 A spokeswoman from the Consumer Association said, 'Consumers should probably try to avoid buying dairy products from France just at the moment, until more is known about the disease.'

The spokeswoman discouraged _____
_____ .

8 The head of the airline said, 'If the competition continue to drop their prices like this, we will be forced to do the same and then there will be a price war which will benefit no-one.'

The head of the airline threatened _____
_____ .

Reading

8 Read the article on bloggers from *The Guardian* newspaper and then match each statement (1–8) with one of the paragraphs (A–E). You will need to use some of the letters more than once.

Learning to love the bloggers

A

The rise of online social networks such as MySpace, Bebo and Facebook, has been one of the most dramatic developments on the web over the past few years. But the business world has struggled to come to terms with the increase of user-generated content such as blogs and video diaries. The huge size of online communities such as MySpace has already brought Google and Yahoo! into these sites, looking to attract new users to their search engines.

B

Much that has been written about the blogosphere has focused on the threat posed to companies by individual consumers, who suddenly have a voice which they can use to complain about a particular product or service. Sites such as NTL: Hell in the UK, which recorded the difficulties and frustrations of consumers who found themselves struggling with the cable company's poor service, have received a lot of coverage.

C

But there are also opportunities available online. A brand that can successfully open up to its critics and, crucially, get them involved in creating a better product, can soon find itself with some key supporters in the online world. Because even though the media world may be fragmenting, there still seems to be a fundamental connection between people and products. According to Matthew Yeomans, 'A hundred years of consumer marketing has shown that the public is actually very receptive to brands and wants to embrace them.'

D

Anthony Mayfield, head of content and media at the online marketing firm Spannerworks, said: 'Everything is changing about how media works; we are moving from an age of channel media – where infrastructure and content and distribution is owned by organisations – to one where everybody can play a part. That does not mean those organisations go away; there are just a lot more people out there creating and distributing content.'

E

That change from the old model of one media outlet 'broadcasting' to the masses demands a shift in the way that brands and businesses try to get their message across. How brands and businesses use social networks is more complicated than the old advertising model. Bloggers detest intrusive marketing in their personal space online. As a result, advertising to the blogging community needs to be much more inclusive and more of a dialogue than merely shouting a particular message, usually through banner adverts, hoping someone will hear it.

0 Although communication channels are different now, people are still fascinated by products. *C*

1 Companies will need to change the way that they communicate to consumers. _____

2 Companies can benefit from dialogue with people who criticise its products online. _____

3 A new danger for companies is that a single customer's dissatisfaction can get a big audience. _____

4 Companies have found it difficult to adapt to the sudden rise in online social networks. _____

5 Organisations are no longer the only ones to control media content. _____

6 New online networks have attracted interest simply by being so large. _____

7 Bloggers hate to receive advertising messages on their own web pages. _____

8 The new online social networks will not kill off the old media companies. _____

3.2 Email exchange

Formal and informal emails

1 Convert the following formal email into an informal one by changing the underlined words.

Dear Didier

(0) <u>Thank you</u> Thanks for offering to (1) <u>assist</u> me with the Blane report. The chairman specifically (2) <u>proposed that I should</u> compile it and, (3) <u>therefore</u>, I (4) <u>do not</u> feel I (5) <u>am able to</u> accept your kind offer. (6) <u>However,</u> (7) <u>I would be very grateful if you could</u> send me any relevant information that might help me with it. (8) <u>Do not hesitate to</u> call me if you (9) <u>wish</u> to discuss it (10) <u>further</u>.

Kind regards

Jean

---

2 Convert the following informal email into a formal one by changing the underlined words. Use the words in the box to help you (in most cases you will need to use other words too).

> contact   do not   soon   prefer   sincerely
> grateful   will   currently   meantime   apologise
> my apologies   send   ~~thank~~

Dear Ms Doyle

(0) <u>Thanks</u> Thank you for your email. (1) <u>I'm sorry</u> for the delay in sending you the T-shirt that you ordered. (2) <u>At the moment,</u> we (3) <u>don't</u> have the medium size you asked for in stock. We hope to have delivery of these on Friday. (4) <u>The moment</u> they arrive, (5) <u>I'll</u> (6) <u>get</u> one out to you by first class post. Or, if (7) <u>it's better for you</u>, I can send you either a small or large T-shirt of the same design immediately. If this is the case, (8) <u>please</u> (9) <u>get in touch</u> and let me know. (10) <u>For now,</u> I will try to get the medium size in as soon as possible.

(11) <u>Sorry</u> once again.

(12) <u>Best wishes</u>

Gareth Evans

---

3 Choose a linking word or phrase from the box to fill each gap. (Some words are not needed.)

> since   however   nevertheless   besides
> ~~owing to~~   anyway   in the meantime
> consequently   although   following
> subsequently   moreover

Dear David

In response to your request, I am writing with an update on the construction of the new PB1 headquarters in Shanghai.

(0) Owing to difficulties obtaining planning permission, work has not in fact begun yet. As you know, there were some features of the original design which the local planning authorities were not happy with and, (1) _____ , we have had to submit modified plans. We are not anticipating any problems with these changes, but,

(2) _____ , we will have to wait for formal permission before starting work.

(3) _____ , we have been able to start construction of the access road to the building. This work is progressing well and will be completed in time for the main construction.

(4) _____ , it will also be on budget.

(5) _____ the withdrawal of Jarjing Inc, one of the building subcontractors, we have had to look for a replacement. (6) _____ , this is not something that we want to rush.

(7) _____ , we already have two subcontractors who can begin the work when permission is granted. (8) _____ we need to find the right partner, we have invited about ten firms to bid for the contract and we expect to make a decision within the next eight weeks.

I hope this gives you enough information. Please do not hesitate to call me if there are further details you require.

Best regards

Mei Ling

3.3 Listening Test: Part One

Predicting what word(s) will go into each space is a key skill in Part One of the Listening Test.

1 Study the sentences in the seminar notes below and predict what kind of word(s) will go into each gap. The missing word(s) or phrase(s) might be a date, a name, an adjective, an adverb, a verb phrase etc.

2 Read the statements about Part One of the Listening Test and mark them *True* or *False*.

1 Correct spelling of the missing words is not so important.

2 Don't write the exact words you hear in the recording.

3 It helps to understand the context of the passage first.

4 Don't get stuck on a particular question; you will have a second chance to listen.

5 It's better to leave a space blank than write in a guess.

IMPACTO SEMINAR

Introduction

1 Impacto was founded in _____ .

2 It specialises in improving business people's _____

3 Most business people communicate _____ .

4 This is a one-day taster course, but you can follow courses for up to _____ .

Good communication

5 Good communication is about feeling _____ .

6 If you can show this quality, other people will _____ .

7 What we aim to do is bring out your _____ .

8 It's also very important to understand the dynamics of _____ .

The main topics

9 Today we are going to look at dealing with difficult _____

10 Everyone finds themselves in situations which are _____

11 We will use video case studies, demonstrations and _____ .

12 As you leave you can help yourself to a _____ .

4.1 The art of selling

Selling

1 Match each word on the left with a word on the right to make sales and marketing collocations.

0	prospective	A	maker
1	emotional	B	advantage
2	buying	C	customer
3	unique	D	service
4	payment	E	technique
5	sales	F	terms
6	competitive	G	signal
7	price	H	benefits
8	decision	I	value
9	added	J	selling point
10	after-sales	K	competition

2 Read the descriptions of each sales promotion medium and then complete its name.

0 Putting a message on company vans or an advertisement on a bus or taxi: _vehicle advertising_

1 By far the cheapest and most effective form of advertising: w _____ o _____ m _____

2 Typically used for sporting events to raise awareness of the company's brand: s _____

3 Used by companies to sell a particular product at a retail outlet, eg a supermarket: p _____ o _____ s _____ promotion

4 Large advertisements placed by the side of the road to attract the attention of motorists: b _____

5 Cheap form of promotion, but not that effective as most people throw it away: d _____ m _____

6 Increasingly popular form of Internet advertising that relies on people passing the advertisement to friends and colleagues: v _____ m _____

3 Choose the best word (A–D) for each space (1–6) to complete this article about 'Myths in selling'.

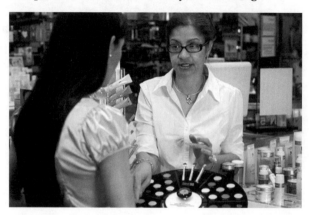

1 **'Buyers are liars.'**

I'm constantly amazed how many salespeople use this expression. Do people (**0**) _____ salespeople? Absolutely. But this usually occurs when the sales person has failed to earn that person's trust. Gaining someone's trust means not (**1**) _____ them into making a (**2**) _____ decision. It means focusing your attention on *their* situation rather than trying to (**3**) _____ the sale. Earning trust means treating people with respect and dignity even if they are not prepared to make a decision right now.

2 **'Anyone can be persuaded to buy.'**

I once heard someone say, 'If you have a strong case you will clarify it. If you have a weak case, you will try and (**4**) _____ the other person.' The real key is to determine whether or not the person or company you are speaking to has a genuine (**5**) _____ for your product or service. If they do not, then your best (**6**) _____ is to move on to someone who does need *and* want your particular solution.

0	A lie	B	mislead	C	falsify	D	fraud
1	A attracting	B	making	C	pushing	D	urging
2	A buying	B	buyer	C	bought	D	buy
3	A finish	B	end	C	close	D	do
4	A dissuade	B	persuade	C	appeal	D	win
5	A interest	B	request	C	need	D	want
6	A way	B	strategy	C	advantage	D	terms

Tenses and time phrases

4 Complete this memo from a branch manager of a bank to her marketing director by putting each verb in brackets into the correct tense.

> ### INTERNAL MEMO
>
> TO: David Cooper
> FROM: Maria Nieto
> SUBJECT: Home insurance offer
>
> Hi David
>
> You **(0)** asked (ask) me for an update on the home insurance offer that the bank **(1)** _____ (launch) last month. This is what I can tell you based on the data that I **(2)** _____ (collect) so far.
>
> Since the launch, we **(3)** _____ (circulate) about 8,000 leaflets to our customers with their monthly statements. Up to now, the response **(4)** _____ (be) quite low – about two percent. By response, I mean people who have requested more information. I expect that by the end of the month most of these people **(5)** _____ (decide) whether to take up the offer or not. I will of course send you these figures.
>
> I have to say, I am not so surprised at the low response. These days, private customers **(6)** _____ (tend) to go to one provider for all their insurance – car, house, travel, etc – and that means an insurance company.
>
> As you know, currently the bank **(7)** _____ (look) into the possibility of offering these other types of insurance and I think that when we do, the response will be much better.
>
> I **(8)** _____ (write) to you again in a couple of weeks to give you a further update. In the meantime, please contact me if you would like to discuss any of the above.
>
> Best wishes
>
> Maria

5 Replace the underlined time phrase in each sentence with the phrase from the box that is most similar in meaning.

> currently   in the past   sooner or later
> in the last decade   up to now
> since I was born   ~~these days~~

0 <u>Nowadays</u> people expect their cars to be completely reliable. These days

1 <u>So far</u>, we have spent a very small amount of money on advertising. _____

2 <u>Over the past 10 years</u>, the price of oil has more than doubled. _____

3 <u>In time</u>, people will realise what a great product this is. _____

4 <u>At the moment</u> we are developing a new range of women's fashion accessories. _____

5 <u>Formerly</u>, I worked as a sales advisor for a large bank. _____

6 I have lived in Berlin <u>all my life</u>. _____

Transitive and intransitive verbs

6 Some of the following sentences use a transitive verb when an intransitive verb is needed and vice versa. Decide which sentences are correct (✓) and which sentences are incorrect (✗).

0 If we fall the number of people working on the project, it won't be finished in time. (*reduce*) ☒

1 Our chances of finding a solution are decreasing every day. ☐

2 He rose everyone's hopes of getting a bonus and then announced there would be none. ☐

3 The share price dropped quite dramatically when the government cancelled the contract. ☐

4 The quality of TV programmes has reduced a lot since I was a boy. ☐

5 The bank will probably raise interest rates again this month. ☐

6 The size of the engine has been reduced, but it still produces the same amount of power. ☐

7 How can we rise productivity when the staff feel so insecure? ☐

8 When we have a bigger volume of sales, we can think about declining the price. ☐

7 Complete this telephone conversation between a buyer and a supplier of bath towels. The first letter of each missing word has been given for you.

Supplier Hi, Tracey. How's business?

Buyer Very good thanks. The (**0**) trial we ran with your 'Comfort' range went very well.

Supplier So, you'll be (**1**) p _____ an order soon?

Buyer Yes, I'd like to. Just remind me what the (**2**) d _____ time is.

Supplier We're quoting two weeks for items that we have in (**3**) s _____ .

Buyer OK. And my sales (**4**) c _____ is still as agreed, 40%?

Supplier That's right, 40% of the recommended retail price, which is the price you must sell at – you can't (**5**) m _____ up the price further. What kind of (**6**) v _____ of sales are you anticipating?

Buyer I'm expecting to sell a lot. The idea is to get Selman's to carry the range right across their (**7**) c _____ of stores. I'll phone the order through next week.

Supplier That's excellent news. You'll need more (**8**) p _____ material. I'll send you 300 catalogues and six display stands.

Pronunciation

8 Verbs ending *-ed* can be pronounced in one of three ways: /d/ *arrived* /t/ *stopped* /id/ *wanted*
Look at the following verbs ending *-ed* and say which way each is pronounced.

increased slightly /t/	changed very little
picked up	ended the year
plummeted	reached a peak
recovered slowly	decreased sharply
fluctuated	rocketed
stayed the same	gradually levelled off
developed	recorded a rise
dropped	

9 Match each of the descriptions in the box to one of the graphs below.

fluctuated wildly   ~~recorded a sharp rise~~
increased steadily   diverged significantly
developed in a similar way   reached a peak
remained relatively stable   recovered slightly
continued on an upward trend with some fluctuations

0

recorded a sharp rise

1

_____

2

_____

3

_____

4

_____

5

_____

6

_____

7

_____

8

_____

4.2 Presenting figures

Describing performance

1 Put the correct preposition in each gap to complete the presentation. In some cases more than one answer may be possible.

The graph shows the levels of the country's imports and exports (**0**) *over / during* the period 1990 to 2000. If we look (**1**) _____ imports first, we can see that they increased quite dramatically over the period (**2**) _____ question (**3**) _____ $24 billion to $53 billion. (**4**) _____ contrast, exports fell, though not (**5**) _____ the same extent. From a level of $60 billion in 1990, exports fell to $31 billion in 2000, a fall (**6**) _____ 50%. This was not at all in line (**7**) _____ the forecasts for the economy: the trade surplus of the early 90's had been converted (**8**) _____ a trade deficit (**9**) _____ the end of the decade. (**10**) _____ the same time the country had failed to grow their export market.

---

2 Complete the sales presentation about two recently launched computer games using the phrases from the box.

As you can see
In conclusion
If we look at the first graph
The second graph shows
Now if there are any questions
Thanks for your attention
Comparing the two
I'm going to present
~~Thank you, everyone, for coming today.~~

(**0**) Thank you, everyone, for coming today. I'm really glad to have this opportunity to tell you how City Cop 2 and Alligator are doing since their launch, and I know that you're all keen to know! So, today (**1**) _____ the results of the first six months' sales. (**2**) _____ , we can see that sales of City Cop 2 were slow at first, but really took off in month three. We don't have any real explanation for this; we're just happy that the market responded. (**3**) _____ , sales have continued to increase rapidly from that time and last month reached 48,000 units. (**4**) _____ sales of Alligator over the same period. This had a good start and recorded a healthy level of sales in the first six months, rising from 16,000 per month to 23,000 units. (**5**) _____ , it's clear that City Cop 2 is on a more rapidly rising curve than Alligator. (**6**) _____ , I would say that the results are very encouraging and pretty much in line with our forecasts. (**7**) _____ .
(**8**) _____ , I'll do my best to answer them.

3 Read the questions and answers below. Rewrite each answer in three different ways, beginning as shown. All answers should have the same meaning.

Question: *What effect did the warm winter temperatures have on the ski resort of St Anton?*
Answer: *A lot of people cancelled their holidays.*

0 The result was that a lot of people cancelled their holidays.

1 It resulted _____ .

2 It led _____ .

3 It meant _____ .

Question: *How was such a small company able to compete with the big computer games companies?*
Answer: *They had very talented software designers.*

00 It was because they had very talented software designers.

4 It was on account _____ .

5 It was thanks _____ .

6 It had a lot to do _____ .

4.3 Writing Test: Part One

1 **Decide which of the following tips for answering Part One of the Writing Test are true (T) and which are false (F).**

0 You should begin by describing what the graphs illustrate. T

1 You should use the exact words given in the question to do this. _____

2 You should divide your description into clear paragraphs. _____

3 You should describe in detail the development of each curve. _____

4 You should draw a general conclusion from the information presented. _____

5 You should give reasons for each change in the development. _____

6 You do not need to describe the figures accurately. _____

2 **Answer the following exam question, using the framework given to help you. Then compare your answer with the model answer on page 70.**

Framework

- Begin by describing what the graph is intended to show.
- Describe the general development.
- Describe briefly the development of each of the three curves, comparing them where necessary.
- Write a conclusion about what the graph tells you about the company's activity.

PART ONE

Question 1

- The graph below shows production output at three different plants belonging to the same company over the period 2000 to 2005.
- Using the information in the graph, write a short **report** describing the different rates of production and what this means for the company.
- Write **120–140** words.

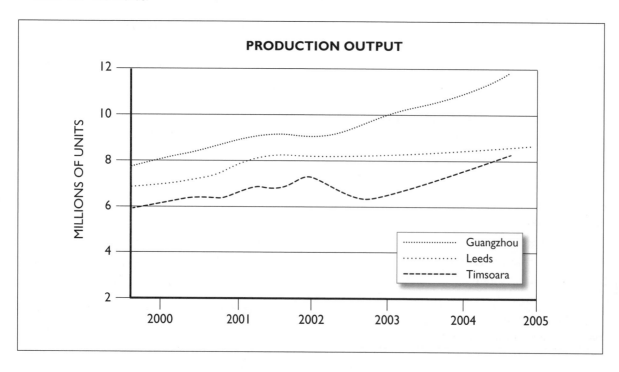

5.1 Money and finance

Money expressions

1 Choose the best word to complete each sentence.

0 We can't say we have (done) / *performed* the deal until we have a signed contract.

1 So far, the business hasn't *lent / borrowed* any money from the bank – it's been self-financing.

2 We've *lost / wasted* a lot of money on consultants whose advice hasn't really benefited the business.

3 The company *made / won* most of its profits from the sale of property.

4 I invest on the stock market as a hobby, but I never really *earn / make* any money.

5 I advise you to get a loan from a commercial bank – they *charge / withdraw* less interest.

6 We have *earned / saved* a lot of money by outsourcing our IT services.

7 My house *costs / is worth* twice what I paid for it ten years ago.

8 They *spent / paid* over £1 million developing the new system.

9 I'm not responding to any more orders until they pay us back what they *owe / borrowed* us.

10 How long will it take you to pay *out / off* the loan?

2 Complete the table to show the correct use of the verbs in the box.

spend   owe   invoice   lend   save   bet   waste
pay   charge

pay	someone money **for** something
	money **on** something

3 Complete the dialogue between a bank manager and a customer applying for a loan by writing one word in each gap.

Bank Manager So, (**0**) how can I help you?

Customer I'd like to (**1**) _____ out a loan to purchase a business premises.

BM I see. I'll just need to take some details. Is your business a limited company?

C Yes. We've been (**2**) _____ business for five years and we're hoping to expand.

BM How (**3**) _____ are you looking to borrow?

C I've found a suitable property which is (**4**) _____ the market for £350,000.

BM And what is the annual (**5**) _____ of your business?

C Our revenue last year was £294,000. From that we (**6**) _____ a £80,000 profit.

BM That sounds healthy. And what can you offer the bank as (**7**) _____ against the loan?

C I own a house myself which is (**8**) _____ about £400,000.

BM And do you (**9**) _____ any money on that?

C I have about £35,000 left to pay.

BM Well, I don't see any problem. I will need you to fill in this form and also to send me your company (**10**) _____ for the last three years.

Pronunciation

4 Generally we don't stress the articles *a, the, some*; auxiliary verbs *have, can, shall, should*; prepositions *to, from, for, of*. Go through the dialogue in exercise 3 again, on your own or with a partner and practise saying it without stressing these words.

Bank Manager So, how <u>can</u> (/kən/) I help you?

Customer I'd like <u>to</u> (/tə/) take out <u>a</u> (/ə/) loan <u>to</u> (/tə/) purchase <u>a</u> (/ə/) business premises.

Expressions of comparison

5 The following sentences are all missing one small word. Write it in.

0 This is *the* last time I'm going to tell you.

1 It's a lot bigger _____ I expected.

2 It's _____ more than I wanted to pay.

3 This is _____ far the best example I've seen.

4 I'm not _____ young _____ I used to be.

5 Can you speak a little _____ slowly, please?

6 Can you speak a little _____ quickly, please?

6 Complete the table of comparative and superlative forms.

Adjective (or adverb)	Comparative form	Superlative form
clever	cleverer	the cleverest
good		the best
quickly		
tiring		the most tiring
bad	worse	
well (adverb)		
far		
little		the least
much	more	

7 Look at the table below and then use the prompts to make sentences about the information in the table.

China / by far / population
China has by far the biggest population of all the countries in the table.

1 Life expectancy in France / much / Russia

2 Russia / slightly / population / Japan

3 Zimbabwe / very similar / Syria

4 The number of internet users in Mexico / much / France

5 Mexico's GDP / not nearly / the USA's

6 China / France / exactly / rate of inflation

7 Japan / very / inflation / compared / USA

8 The USA / by far / country in the table

9 Life expectancy in Zimbabwe / much / other countries

10 Japan's population / twice / France's

Country	Population	GDP per capita $	Unemploy-ment rate	Inflation rate	Life expectancy	Internet users
China	1.321 million	7,600	4.2%	1.5%	72.9 years	123 million
USA	301 million	43,500	4.8%	2.5%	78 years	205 million
Russia	141.3 million	12,100	6.6%	9.8%	65.8 years	23.7 million
Japan	127.5 million	33,100	4.1%	0.3%	82 years	86.3 million
Mexico	108.7 million	10,600	3.2%	3.4%	75.6 years	18.6 million
France	63.7 million	30,100	8.7%	1.5%	80.6 years	30 million
Syria	19.3 million	4,000	12.5%	8%	70.6 years	1.1 million
Zimbabwe	12.3 million	2,000	80%	976.4%	39.5 years	1 million

Company finance

8 Complete the brief descriptions of the main three types of financial statement by putting one financial term in each gap. The first letter has been given for you.

The balance sheet shows the company's

(**0**) assets on one side and its

(**1**) l _____ plus the shareholders

(**2**) e _____ on the other. The two totals are always equal to each other.

The income statement or (profit and

(**3**) l _____ account) shows the

(**4**) t _____ (and other income) of the company less all its operating

(**5**) c _____ (or expenses). The result is the (**6**) g _____ profit. When tax and interest have been deducted you have the

(**7**) n _____ profit, which is the

(**8**) b _____ line.

The cashflow statement shows the money available to the company at a given time to pay its

(**9**) c _____ and to finance new

(**10**) i _____ .

9 Below is an article giving advice to small business owners. Choose one sentence (A–H) to go in each gap (1–6). (One sentence is not needed).

Eight winning tips to make your financial plan profitable

Create a financial plan: Estimate how much revenue you expect to bring in each month, and project what your expenses will be. If you need it, get help from business planning books, software, (**0**) F.

Review the plan monthly: Even if time is taken to prepare a financial plan with profit and loss projections, it often sits in a desk drawer. (**1**) _____ ; you have to review it regularly.

Lost profits can't be recovered: When comparing your projections to reality and finding earnings too low or expenses too high, the conclusion often is, 'I'll make it up later.' The problem is that you really can't make it up later. (**2**) _____ .

Make adjustments right away: If revenues are lower than expected, increase efforts in sales and marketing or look for ways to increase your rates. If overhead costs are too high, find ways to cut back. There are other businesses like yours around. (**3**) _____

Think before you spend: When considering any new business expense, including marketing and sales activities, evaluate the increased earnings you expect to bring in against its cost before you proceed to make a purchase.

Don't be afraid to hire: Retailers and restaurateurs wouldn't consider operating without employees, but many service businesses limit themselves by being understaffed. (**4**) _____ . You can better use your talents for generating revenue than for running errands and filing.

Pay yourself a salary: If you are incorporated, you may already be doing this. (**5**) _____ . Each month that your business meets its profitability goal, pay yourself the full amount. When you miss your target, dock your 'pay' and when you exceed it, pay yourself a 'bonus'.

It's about profit, not revenue: It doesn't matter how many thousands of dollars you are bringing in each month if your expenses are almost as high, or higher. (**6**) _____ . Don't be one of them.

A Almost any business can benefit from hired or contracted help

B Every month profits are too low is a month that is gone forever

C When you get your annual tax bill, it may be too late

D If not, allocate an amount to owner's compensation on a monthly basis

E It's not enough to have a plan

F or ask an accountant

G What is their secret for operating profitably?

H Many high-revenue businesses have gone under for this very reason

10 Write down six different types of cost a manufacturing company has.

Overhead costs

Marketing costs

5.2 Discussing options

1 Write a phrase or sentence to:

0 give your opinion
  As I see it, we should do

1 ask for someone's opinion
  _____

2 make a suggestion
  _____

3 state a preference
  _____

4 agree with someone
  _____

5 disagree politely
  _____

6 suggest an alternative course of action.
  _____

2 Complete each recommendation using one of the endings on the right.

0 My preference would	A rush into making a decision.
1 I think it would be better	B about entering the Chinese market.
2 I have some reservations	C be to develop our markets on all fronts.
3 We shouldn't	D for the eastern European market.
4 The advantage	E the best opportunity.
5 We would be better	F that we wait a year.
6 I think China represents	G to expand slowly.
7 I suggest	H off concentrating on Europe.
8 Personally, I would go	I of Hungary is that it's near.

3 Complete the conversation between a managing director and his deputy director by adding the deputy director's responses from the box in the correct order.

> – Maybe, in the short term, but if we were to pass the cost on, we might lose customers.
> – That's the decision you have to make, but you've heard my opinion now.
> – As I see it, we've got two options. We could absorb the cost or pass it on to our customers.
> – ~~What do you want to know exactly?~~
> – I'd recommend absorbing the cost for now. The price of steel may come down again.

MD I wanted to ask your advice about the rise in steel prices.

DD *What do you want to know exactly?*

MD Well, what do you suggest that we do about it?

DD _____

  _____

MD And which of those two do you recommend?

DD _____

  _____

MD My only reservation about that is that it will hurt our profit margins.

DD _____

  _____

MD I see what you're saying, but wouldn't it be better to lose a few than to be unprofitable?

DD _____

  _____

Read the transcript of the Listening Test, Part Two. Complete Task One as you read each extract the first time; then read the extracts a second time and complete Task Two.

- Read the extracts by five business owners talking about their financial situation.
- For each extract there are two tasks. For Task One, choose the sector their business is in, from the list **A–H**. For Task Two, choose the financial problem each person identifies from the list **A–H**.

TASK ONE – SECTOR

1 _____	**A** car repair
	B clothes retail
2 _____	**C** tourism
	D footwear
3 _____	**E** education
	F property / real estate
4 _____	**G** electrical goods retail
5 _____	**H** mail order firm

TASK TWO – FINANCIAL PROBLEM

1 _____	**A** high material costs
	B investment risk
2 _____	**C** expensive premises
	D no credit rating
3 _____	**E** high cost of advertising
	F being paid late
4 _____	**G** loans to repay
5 _____	**H** High salaries to pay

Transcript

1 Unfortunately for us, most of our business comes from two big clients. Even though we are only a small group of teachers and trainers, we still have to respect these companies' payment terms. In the case of one of them it's 45 days and the other is 60 days, which gives us real problems with cashflow.

2 As a high street shop, cashflow is not a particular problem. It's the rent and local business rates that are so crippling. But because we sell ladies' fashion, location is very important. We could find something much cheaper out of the city centre, but our income would certainly suffer.

3 We borrowed quite a lot of money to set up the business four years ago and I've no regrets. We couldn't have fitted out the garage with the right equipment otherwise – hydraulic ramps, a body-paint shop and so on. It's just that the interest is so high and it means we spend a lot of our time working to service the debt rather than developing the business.

4 It's a great business with very low costs on the whole. We don't have a shop front – we just send out catalogues and people phone in their orders. It can be expensive when we get returns, but the main difficulty is the marketing, because it's so expensive these days. Unless we are present every week in some newspaper or magazine, or on a billboard somewhere, customers forget about us.

5 We are currently buying a lot of small villas and farmhouses in … Well, I won't tell you where in case you get ideas of your own – but it's a small developing country. It's a big gamble, because no-one actually knows whether the market there is going to take off or not. If it doesn't we'll be bankrupted … but I'm confident.

6.1 Purchasing power

Purchasing and supplier relationships

1 Read the extract from an article about consumer protection and choose the best word (A, B, C or D) to fill each gap.

96% of all shopping transactions go (**0**) _____ . But what protection do you have as a consumer from an (**1**) _____ seller? If you buy (**2**) _____ goods you have the right to return them to the seller within seven days and get a full (**3**) _____ refund. Within 28 days you can obtain a credit note for your unwanted purchase. In cases of (**4**) _____ in receiving goods or finding that the goods were not as advertised, you will have more trouble. Even if you have paid (**5**) _____ and acted in good faith, there is no guarantee the seller will do the same. An online trader might, for example, sell you something he doesn't have (**6**) _____ stock. When you complain, he might answer that there has been a 'slight delay in (**7**) _____' and there is little you can do. In the end, if you cannot get satisfactory compensation from the supplier, then your only option is to take your case to a consumer association or small claims court. Unsurprisingly, most people don't bother. They just tell their friends to (**8**) _____ of the company in future.

But what happens if you feel that you have been (**9**) _____ for a product or service? This is a situation that, up to now, even the small courts have not been able to help with. However, in a recent court case a large sportswear retailer was found guilty of selling football shirts at an (**10**) _____ price and fined a six-figure sum.

0 A smoothly   B on   C fluently   D properly
1 A impartial   B unsure   C unreliable   D inept
2 A fallible   B false   C failing   D faulty
3 A exchange   B cash   C monetary   D money
4 A deliveries   B delays   C postponements   D pauses
5 A promptly   B fast   C accurately   D off
6 A at   B on   C in   D with
7 A distribute   B departure   C dismissal   D despatch
8 A beware   B avoid   C distrust   D suspect
9 A overpriced   B oversold   C overcharged   D overdone
10 A excess   B above   C unreasonable   D increasing

2 Complete each definition by writing one word in the gap. The first letter has been written in for you.

0 When you telephone a supplier to order goods or services you place an order.

1 If you wish to continue a contract or agreement on the same terms you ask for an e _____ .

2 Discounting products at certain times of the year, is known as s _____ discounting.

3 A company which uses its purchasing power to force its suppliers to give better and better prices is said to be s _____ them.

4 Materials in their basic state used in manufacturing are called r _____ materials.

5 A contract to be the only agent representing a supplier is called an e _____ contract.

6 If, when your material costs increase, you increase the price to the final customer, then you p _____ the increase on.

7 The conditions in a contract stating when and how a supplier will be paid are called the payment t _____ .

8 The reaction of customers to a particular product or service is known as customer f _____ .

Relative and participial clauses

3 A *competitive tender* is when a company invites various suppliers to quote for a job. Put these steps in the tendering process into the correct order and number them 1–6. (Use a dictionary if you are unsure of any of the terms in italics.)

The owner / commissioning company
☐ Evaluates the *bids / offers*; makes *a shortlist*
☐ *Awards* the contract to a supplier
☐ 1 Launches *a call for tender*, giving the *technical specifications*

Supplier
☐ *Wins / loses* the contract
☐ *Bids for / tenders for* the contract
☐ *Negotiates* the details

4 Read the conditions of a call for tender set out by a company for its suppliers and replace each participial clause with a relative clause for questions 1–4, and vice versa for question 5–8.

0 Suppliers doing more than 50% of their business with us will have to reduce this dependency.
Suppliers <u>which do</u> more than 50% of their business with us will have to reduce this dependency.

1 Any company wishing to be considered must submit their bid by 20 April.

2 Bids submitted after that date will not be considered.

3 Anyone giving inaccurate information will be disqualified.

4 Prices quoted in this initial bid will be treated as negotiable.

00 Potential suppliers who want to find out more details may call 0208 895 6767
Potential suppliers <u>wanting</u> to find out more details may call 0208 895 6767

5 Anyone who questions the terms should contact our contracts office.

6 Companies who are owned by a larger group or parent company must declare this fact.

7 Suppliers who cannot fulfil all the conditions need not apply.

8 The decision which will be made on 14 May will be final.

Tense practice

5 Complete this email by writing each verb in brackets in the correct tense.

Dear Ms Spackman

I (**0**) am writing (write) to you ask a couple of questions about your recently launched call for tender. Actually, this is the second time that we (**1**) _____ (submit) a bid to your company and I hope that this time we (**2**) _____ (be) successful.

My questions are as follows:

1) The technical specifications are exactly the same as the last time we (**3**) _____ (tender) for this contract two years ago. Is this intentional?

2) You ask for three references. How recent must these be? We (**4**) _____ (do) a job of comparable size six years ago but since then, we (**5**) _____ (not / do) anything on the same scale.

For the time being we (**6**) _____ (continue) to work on our offer, but I hope to receive your answers before long.

Yours sincerely

Danny Robinson

A letter of complaint

6 Sentences A–F are extracts from letters of complaint. Read each one and match it to the company it is intended for (1–5).

0 A camera manufacturer who has spent three months repairing a camera.   A

1 An employment agency who supplied an inefficient temporary secretary.   ____

2 A building company who left a job unfinished.   ____

3 An online bookshop which keeps sending out the wrong books.   ____

4 A gas company which has sent an incorrect bill.   ____

5 A consultancy firm that has sent a legal advisor rather than a marketing specialist.   ____

A I am writing concerning the unacceptable delay we have experienced.

B I am writing to complain about what I see as serious negligence on your part.

C I think there has been some misunderstanding.

D It is with much frustration that I find myself writing to you yet again about the incorrect filling of an order.

E Re: Ms Davies
I am writing to express my deep concern about the standard of work of the above.

F I would like to draw to your attention the fact that we have been overcharged for our last three months' consumption.

7 A building company you have hired to renovate your offices has left the job half finished to go and complete another job. The consequence is that your employees are working in unsuitable and unsafe conditions. Write a letter of complaint using the framework below. (200–250 words)

Framework

- the reason for writing
- details of the work that you originally agreed
- details of the work that they have actually completed
- the conditions your employees are working in now
- your next course of action
- closing remarks

Pronunciation

8 Look at these groups of words and say which two contain the same vowel sound.

0 (fill)   (bid)   file
Both contain /ɪ/, file has the sound /aɪ/ as in try.

1	work	walk	learn
2	lawyer	launch	law
3	special	legal	present
4	agent	failure	chat
5	month	honest	front

Telephone expressions

1 Match each telephoning expression on the left with a phrase on the right.

0 to hold on	A to call again with the information needed
1 to hang up	B to phone back
2 to get through to someone	C to put someone through
3 to return a call	D to reach someone
4 to get the wrong number	E to wait
5 to get back to someone	F to put down the receiver
6 to connect someone	G to misdial

2 Complete these telephone exchanges using sentences beginning with *I'll ... .*

0 Can I speak to Fanny, please?
   Of course. I'll *just get her for you.*

1 His line is engaged. Would you like to hold?
   No, that's OK. I'll _____

2 Can I give you the address?
   Sure. One minute, I'll _____

3 Can I speak to someone in technical support?
   One moment. I'll _____

4 Is the correct figure 7.8 or 8.7?
   Hang on, I'll _____

5 I need the information urgently.
   OK. I'll _____

6 Please tell Kevin that I will meet him outside
   210 Regent Street at 10.30.
   OK. I'll _____

7 Do you have the information to hand?
   No, but I'll _____

8 So, 6 o'clock tomorrow at the Red Lion pub in
   George Street.
   Great. I'll _____

3 Rewrite this telephone conversation using idiomatic and natural English.

0 **A** Hello, would it be possible to converse with Mr Fernandez?
   Hello, Can I speak to Mr Fernandez, please?

1 **B** Yes. If you would be patient for a little while. I will confirm whether he is available.
   _____

   A Thank you.

2 **B** I would like to tell him your name, if I may.
   _____

   A Mrs Sarah Jordan.

3 **B** Thank you, Mrs Jordan ... I will transfer your call to his line now.
   _____

4 **C** Hello, this is Mr Fernandez. How may I be of assistance to you?
   _____

5 **A** I am telephoning you from Mcmillion Publishers. The purpose of this telephone call is to enquire whether you will be attending the book launch this evening.
   _____
   _____

6 **C** One moment, please. I will consult my diary. I regret that I have another engagement this evening.
   _____
   _____

7 **A** Don't be concerned. It will be repeated on 12 May. Is that date convenient?
   _____
   _____

8 **C** Perhaps. I will have to telephone you again when I have more information.
   _____

9 **A** It will be a pleasure to hear from you.
   _____

1 Read the exam question: What kind of letter are you going to write?

Register:

A formal

B semi-formal

C informal

Tone:

A apologetic

B sympathetic

C firm and unsympathetic

Content:

A accepting full responsibility

B suggesting a compromise

C denying responsibility

PART TWO
Question 1

- You represent a company that makes and fits swimming pools for private customers. A customer has complained that the heater you supplied for his pool is not powerful enough to heat the water sufficiently and is threatening legal action.

- Write a **letter** to the customer:
  - acknowledging his problem
  - pointing out he was originally offered a choice of heaters (and chose a smaller one)
  - explaining that this is not your financial responsibility
  - suggesting other possibilities to rectify the situation (eg a bigger heater)
  - mentioning what the next step is.

---

2 Write in the missing words (1–8) to complete the framework of the letter.

> ≈ **WaterWorld** ≈
>
> Dear Mr Opik
>
> I apologise (**0**) for missing your recent call concerning your new pool. I was also sorry and surprised to hear that you have (**1**) _____ problems with it so soon.
>
> (**2**) _____ you will recall, when we originally discussed _____ _____ _____ _____ _____ _____ _____ _____
>
> As a (**3**) _____ of this, we feel that it is not _____ _____ _____ _____
>
> In (**4**) _____ to resolve this problem, I suggest that _____ _____ _____
>
> If you like, I would be very (**5**) _____ to come _____ _____ _____
>
> I look forward to (**6**) _____ (**7**) _____ you
>
> Yours (**8**) _____
>
> Selma Chakrabati

3 Complete the letter, adding the necessary details around this framework. Write 200–250 words.

7.1 Managing people

Managerial qualities

1 Complete each phrase (1–10) with the most appropriate ending (A–K).

'The most important thing for a manager to learn is how to ...'

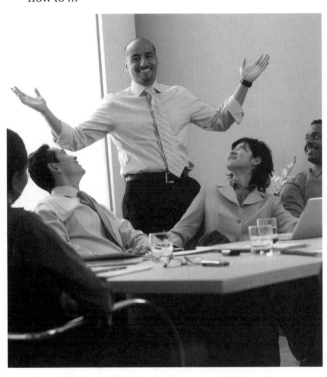

0	recognise and reward	A	responsibility
1	motivate	B	his / her team
2	delegate	C	work efficiently
3	make	D	with all other departments
4	cooperate	E	good performance
5	lead	F	between what is a priority and what is not
6	set	G	quick decisions
7	organise	H	his / her ideas clearly
8	deal with	I	by example
9	distinguish	J	clear objectives
10	communicate	K	difficult people

2 Read the conversations and write the most suitable idiom in each gap. You may need to make changes, to verb forms or pronouns, for example.

spread oneself very thin	take it on board
put people on the spot	~~hands on~~
bite off more than you can chew	
open a can of worms	cut corners
get on with	get one's hands dirty

'The job is probably more (**0**) *hands on* than you had in mind. How do you feel about going out to work in the field with a team of engineers?'

'I'm not afraid to (**1**) _____ and generally I (**2**) _____ engineers very well. I was one myself for twenty years!'

'How are you finding working with Ji Sung? He's quite demanding isn't he?'

'Well, he (**3**) _____ quite often, but actually, I like to be challenged. The problem is that he tries to do too many things himself – he (**4**) _____ .'

'Look, the boss wants this done properly; the cost is not the first priority.'

'Don't worry, I will (**5**) _____ . We are not going to (**6**) _____ on this job.'

'Are you sure you can find the time to do this? It's a lot of work and I don't want you to (**7**) _____ .'

Finding the time is not what I'm worried about. I'm more concerned that by investigating all these employees' expenses, we are going to (**8**) _____ .'

Pronunciation

3 Decide whether the words in each pair below have the same vowel sounds or different vowel sounds.

			same	different
0	know	no	✓	
1	can	can't		
2	board	bored		
3	first	fast		
4	lead	lied		
5	peace	piece		
6	weight	wait		
7	want	won't		

Expressing purpose

4 Read the reasons that different people give for taking an MBA. Complete each one using the expression of purpose in brackets with the correct verb pattern.

0 I did an MBA (so that / be) better prepared for the world of work.
  I did an MBA *so that I would be* better prepared for the world of work.

1 Actually, I did an MBA (avoid / have) to look for a job immediately.

2 My main motivation was (just /understand) business better.

3 I wanted to do an MBA (in order / meet) people from different backgrounds.

4 I waited until I was 33 to do my MBA (so that / get) the maximum benefit from it.

5 I did the MBA just (in case / be) useful in later life.

6 I was sent on an MBA by my insecure boss (prevent / me / take) over his job!

5 Complete the sentences by thinking of ways to improve different aspects of your English.

0 I am going to *take every opportunity to speak English* so that I can become more fluent.

1 I am going to ＿＿＿＿＿＿＿＿ to expand my vocabulary.

2 I am going to ＿＿＿＿＿＿＿＿ in order to improve my pronunciation.

3 I am going to ＿＿＿＿＿＿＿＿ in case I am asked to speak English at a job interview.

4 I am going to make a list of my most common mistakes to avoid ＿＿＿＿＿＿＿＿ .

5 I am going to read more business magazines in order to ＿＿＿＿＿＿＿＿ .

6 I am going to watch more English TV so that ＿＿＿＿＿＿＿＿ .

Word order: adverbs

6 Rearrange the words to make sentences.

0 I / tomorrow / can / give / certainly / you / an answer
  I can certainly give you an answer tomorrow.

1 She / keeps / rarely / waiting / anyone

2 He / best / under pressure / performs

3 He / at / never / his desk / is

4 If / want / you / properly / something / done / yourself / it / do

5 I / was / exhausted / completely / the trip / after

6 Please / at this address / me / send / every Monday / an update

7 They / next month / their headquarters / to Shanghai / will move

Reading

7 Read the text and underline the phrases in the text which answer the following questions:

1 According to the survey almost 50% of managers believe that ...
2 The results of the survey of employees show that ...
3 What has cost the economy £40 billion?
4 The term 'bottom slicing' means ...
5 The lesson we can learn from sport is that ...
6 The effect of forced ranking on the workforce is ...
7 The art of management is to ...

8 Choose the best option to answer the questions in exercise 7.

1 A the workforce can be reduced by a bit each year.
  B 5% of the workforce is lazy.
  C 20% of the workforce can be fired.
  D targets are more important than jobs.

2 A employees have no confidence in management.
  B employees don't respect their managers.
  C managers have failed to motivate their staff.
  D productivity is not a priority for companies.

3 A Strikes and poor industrial relations.
  B People taking sick leave.
  C Management bonuses.
  D Employees not feeling committed to their jobs.

4 A getting rid of the least effective employees.
  B cutting costs.
  C making the employees responsible for targets.
  D paying employees less when they underperform.

5 A gifted individuals can make all the difference.
  B talented individuals are not always team players.
  C the best teams are not always made up of the best players.
  D talent is very subjective.

6 A to make the recruitment process more efficient.
  B to help them work together as a team.
  C to improve their individual performance.
  D to make them afraid that someone else will take their job.

7 A create a sense of magic.
  B get the best out of what you've got.
  C look after the most talented in the organisation.
  D manage resources carefully.

What sort of boss really cares about his staff?

A survey by management consultancy Hudson has found that one in six senior executives think they could get rid of 20% of employees without damaging performance or morale. Nearly half reckon firing up to 5% a year would be a good thing. Even though only 4% actually carry out this threat, it is still a revealing finding. This is what executives really think of their 'most valued asset': something to be disposed of against a mechanical target.

In another survey, only 38% of employees feel senior managers treat them with respect. Around a quarter of employees rarely or never look forward to going to work, and almost half are leaving or trying to. 'The findings suggest many managers aren't doing enough to keep their staff interested,' said Mike Emmott. The result: underperformance, low productivity and high staff turnover.

The last UK survey for Gallup's Employee Engagement Index makes similar conclusions. In 2005 just 16% of UK employees were 'positively engaged' – loyal and committed to the organisation. Gallup puts the cost to the economy of active disengagement at £40 billion, as employees express their disenchantment by going sick, not trying, leaving, or threatening strikes. The culprit, says Gallup, is poor management. 'Workers say they don't know what is expected of them and managers don't care about them as people.'

In a perverted way, then, employers are right when they say there's something the matter with their workforce. It's just that they are kidding themselves about where the blame lies. In any case, bottom-slicing the 'worst' employees is likely to make things worse, not better. Yes, forced ranking is a way of life at General Electric, and Microsoft does it too, but there is no evidence that it is linked to their success and in most cases it usually does more harm than good.

Forced ranking rests on the idea that the performance of the whole is the sum of those of the individual parts. But the sports pages confirm that teams with the most talented individuals don't always win. Of course, individual ability makes a difference. Sometimes companies do have to get rid of people, particularly if they recruit them incompetently. But forced ranking introduces fear and competition, and while in (economic) theory these optimise individual performance, in (management) practice they damage collective performance. This is the authentic magic of management: getting outstanding performance from 'ordinary' resources by multiplying individual and organisational talent.

7.2 Report writing

A business report

1 The following list contains elements that are all important in report writing. Mark those you think are the essential points (++) and those you think are important (+).

- Answer all the points you have been asked to address accurately. ☐
- Begin with a clear introduction of the aims of the report. ☐
- End with a definite conclusion and recommendation. ☐
- Use sub-headings and bullet points to make the report clearer. ☐
- Be consistent in your arguments and connect your ideas with linking expressions. ☐
- Use language naturally, appropriately and with a minimum of errors. ☐
- Use sophisticated vocabulary and grammatical structure. ☐
- Organise the report so that it is clear which point is being addressed. ☐

2 This report makes some recommendations for a company planning to buy new computers. It is well organised, concise and relevant. But it contains several mistakes in grammar and spelling which are underlined. Correct the mistakes.

0 *to present*

To: Said Kamal

Re: New computers

The aim of this report is (**0**) <u>presenting</u> the best (**1**) <u>choose</u> for the company in replacing its computers in the central administration offices. Following some (**2**) <u>initially</u> research, we narrowed the field down to three possibilities:

The first, DX590, is the (**3**) <u>more</u> expensive of the three, (**4**) <u>with</u> a cost of $590 per unit. However, it is the most (**5**) <u>powerfull</u> and adaptable. The second, the

---

HS Venturer, is a little cheaper to purchase, at $555, but has a smaller hard disk capacity and a slower processor. The third, the Songsing AF100, is (**6**) <u>the</u> bargain at $480 and has similar specifications to the HS Venturer. However, Songsing is a relatively new company and thus it is difficult (**7**) <u>getting</u> references for the product.

(**8**) <u>The another</u> very important factor is the after-sales package. (**9**) <u>Every</u> three companies offer between 1 and 3-year service (**10**) <u>garantees</u>, but on slightly different terms and at different prices. The best of these is the DX590's two-year warranty, (**11**) <u>that</u> is an on-site 24-hour repair service.

In conclusion, we recommend (**12**) <u>to purchase</u> the DX590. The HS Venturer offers much less for a similar price, while the Songsing AF100 is probably too risky, because it has (**13**) <u>any</u> track record. With good service back-up, the DX590 (**14**) <u>can</u> also prove to be the most economical (**15**) <u>on</u> the long run.

3 Connect the ideas in this report with a linking phrase from the box. (Some phrases are not needed.)

on the whole	due to	although	however
in conclusion	since	indeed	consequently
~~Thirdly~~			

(**0**) Thirdly, there is the Giordano Centre in York.
(**1**) _____ we didn't have a lot of time to visit, what we saw impressed us. There are quite a few suitable hotels in the area, all within easy walking distance of the conference centre.
(**2**) _____ , they are reasonably priced.
(**3**) _____ , bookings would have to be made early, (**4**) _____ demand for rooms rises quite dramatically in the summer season. (**5**) _____ , this seems to be the case with all the venues under consideration, so an early decision is recommended.

Do Part Two of the Reading Test. Give yourself 10–12 minutes to complete the task.

PART TWO

- Read this text about work–life balance.
- Choose the best sentence **A–H** to fill each of the gaps **1–6**.
- Do not use any letter more than once.
- There is an example at the beginning (**0**).

Business life: Uncomfortable truths about the work-life balance

Balancing work and life is an unattainable goal. At least, it is for anyone who wants to get ahead. 'Simply cutting back on work inevitably fails, because in real life, success in work is predicated on achievement,' Mr Hammonds writes. 'In a competitive business environment leadership requires commitment, passion and a lot of time.'

It is not just that people who want to leave the office at a reasonable time are competing against those who work until the early hours. (**0**) *G* Pavan Vishwakarma is a freelance software developer who lives in Bhopal and who advertises himself as being available at any time. Do you want balance? Vishwakarma doesn't. (**1**) .... If you're competing against Pavan Vishwakarma – and ultimately, we all are – you can't have both a big paycheck and reasonable hours. (**2**) ....

It is not that work-life balance is not worth having. (**3**) .... It is just that it has its price, which is that you are not going to rise as high in the organisation or be as rich as those who have no interest in work-life balance. You can work more intelligently, and delegate as much as you like, but if you are the sort of person who, faced with a choice between a school play and a crucial meeting, opts for the play, you will fall behind those who would not dream of missing the meeting.

Show me a high-riding chief executive, or a successful politician. (**4**) ....

There is no point, as Mr Hammonds rightly argues, in pretending we can have it all. We can't. The usually unspoken truth about work-life balance is that if you want a life, you have to surrender some of the rewards of work. Those who opt for children, spouse and friends will be richer in all the ways that really count. (**5**) ....

Of course, for most people, all this is academic. They cannot afford to earn less. (**6**) .... For them, life is an endless struggle to find jobs, put food on the table, arrange childcare – and hope that grandparents can step in when children wake up covered in chicken pox. Those who can afford to trade promotion and salary for family time are a lucky minority.

A They can barely get by as it is.

B I will show you someone who barely sees his or her children.

C A few superhuman people may be able to achieve this.

D He wants to work, and he'll work cheap – a lot cheaper than you will.

E However, unless they win the lottery, they will have less money in the bank.

F The laws of economics won't allow it.

G They are also, increasingly, competing against people on the other side of the world who are ready to work any hours.

H It certainly is.

Environmental problems

1   **Read the letter to the editor of the *Financial Times* and answer these questions:**

1. What prompted the author to write the letter?
2. What does he criticise supermarkets for?
3. What point does he make about the cost of energy?
4. What does he mean when he says 'thrift carries little weight'?
5. What does he say will happen if consumers begin to take a stand against this waste?

HALT ALL THIS MINDLESS WASTE OF ENERGY

Sir, H Woolf (Letters, March 15) laments the waste of energy caused by unnecessary lighting and air conditioning in hotel rooms. He is obviously right but why single out the hotel industry?

Like him I live in a world where high street shops keep their doors wide open, with the heating or air conditioning on, throughout the year. A world where office buildings, shops, shopping centres, sports centres, airports, and yes, hotels, keep the lights on throughout the day, and of course at night, whether anyone needs them on or not. A world where office computers stay on all the time and supermarkets present chilled and even frozen food in completely open cooling units. A world where flashy flat screens display useless information to indifferent passers-by. A world where light pollution is practically impossible to fight by legal means. The list goes on.

This mindless waste illustrates two simple facts. First, for much public use energy is cheap and would still be cheap at twice the price. Second, thrift and consideration for the public good carry little weight.

So what can one do? Stop spending money with organisations that accept or even encourage waste, and in the absence of choice, voice disapproval firmly and openly. If enough people do this, the tipping point will be reached very quickly and most of us will be better off for it.

P. Dubois-Pèlerin

2   **Underline the part of the text that means:**

1. The hotel industry is just the tip of the iceberg
2. People who take no notice
3. Consumers should vote with their feet

3   **What can supermarkets in particular do to help the environment? Make two sentences about each of the following:**

Waste:

They can put labels on products with instructions on how to recycle them.

_____

Transport:

_____

_____

Energy:

_____

_____

Suppliers:

_____

_____

4   **Match the environmental problem from the box with the correct definition 1–5.**

flooding   drought   smog   ~~hurricane~~   extinction   leak

0. A violent wind that destroys buildings and trees:
   hurricane
1. A cloud of air pollution that hangs over big cities:
   _____
2. The disappearance of a species of animal or plant:
   _____
3. A long period without rain: _____
4. The escape of a dangerous substance into the local environment: _____
5. An excess of water which submerges roads and buildings: _____

Use of prepositions with statistics

5 The table shows the impressive performance of two uranium mining companies on the Australian stock market. Make sentences about the data using the words given. Make sure you use the correct prepositions.

Price Aus$	Jan	Feb	Mar	Apr	May	Jun
Formetal	3.6	4.2	4.2	4.2	4.8	5.4
Uromin	2.4	2.8	3.2	3.0	3.7	3.6

0 stood / January
Uromin shares stood at $2.4 in January.

1 increased / $1.2 / the six-month period
_____

2 stayed / the same level / three months
_____

3 average / both / showed a rise / 50%
_____

4 climbed / $5.4 / the end of June
_____

5 reached a peak / $3.7 / May
_____

Gerund and infinitive

6 Complete these statements by putting a verb (gerund or infinitive) into each gap.

0 Are you able *to repair* the fault or not? If not, I will go to another garage.

1 It's no use _____ Paolo. He won't know the answer.

2 It's not too late _____ your mind. The job is still available.

3 It takes time _____ a new brand.

4 Stop _____ . Everything will be alright.

5 You can't succeed in business without _____ some risks.

6 It's better _____ a small part of something big than a big part of something small.

7 It's worth _____ £100 extra for a business class seat. It's much more comfortable.

8 I always tell a little joke or story before _____ my presentation.

7 What particular construction do these verbs take after them?

to be committed
to get used
to look forward
to object

} _____

Modal verbs

8 Below are some notices and signs from a trade exhibition. Explain what each one means using *may, should, shouldn't, must, mustn't, don't have to.*

> **PLEASE USE OTHER DOOR**

0 *You shouldn't use this door.*

> **MEETING ROOM 6**
> **Knock and enter**

1 _____

> **No Photography in Main Hall**

2 _____

> **AUTHORIZED PERSONNEL ONLY**

3 _____

> **Present badges HERE (except staff)**

4 _____

> **REGISTER HERE**

5 _____

> **Events catalogue Please take one**

6 _____

Corporate social responsibility

9 Complete the list of key elements of corporate social responsibility by matching the two halves of each statement.

Corporate social responsibility means …	
0 getting involved	A in fighting poverty, unemployment and social injustice
1 being accountable	B for your environment
2 considering	C to growing your business by ethical means
3 taking account	D in projects that benefit the community
4 embracing	E to disclose information
5 taking responsibility	F to the outside world for your actions
6 playing a part	G of the impact of your actions
7 being committed	H the challenge of doing business in a sustainable way
8 being prepared	I the welfare of your employees

10 Complete the text by putting ONE word in each gap.

In 2006, Coca-Cola HBC published its Corporate Social Responsibility report, providing extensive data related to its compliance (**0**) *with* international standards. The company (**1**) _____ continually upgrading its commitments in four key areas: the marketplace, the workplace, the environment, and the community.

Among the many areas of progress, the report notes (**2**) _____ it is addressing concerns about climate change (**3**) _____ acting to reduce its 'carbon footprint'. It has taken a leading role in developing responsible marketing regulations. (**4**) _____ includes the development of a number of its own wellness products and (**5**) _____ restrictions on the promotion of products to underage youngsters. The 2006 CSR report is (**6**) _____ clearest illustration yet of how an industry member is seeking to meet its goals for sustainability.

11 Complete the table.

Adjective	Noun
accountable	accountability
sustainable	
	injustice
poor	
	environment
committed	
involved	
	respect
	benefit
honest	
	consideration

Pronunciation

12 Check your pronunciation. Mark where the stress falls in each of the words in exercise 11. (You will find the rules in Unit 2 helpful). Check for other rules on the answer page when you have finished the exercise.

ac**cou**ntable   accounta**bi**lity

8.2 Formal meetings

1 Think of a suitable phrase for each of the following situations in a meeting:

0 Everyone is present and you want to start.
  OK. Shall we start?

1 You want to know what points are going to be discussed.

_____

2 You want to interrupt the person speaking to make a comment.

_____

3 You want to stop (politely) another person interrupting you.

_____

4 You want to get on to the next point in the meeting.

_____

5 You think it's time for a break.

_____

6 You think that the discussion has got stuck on one point.

_____

7 You want to praise someone for their contribution.

_____

8 You want everyone to hurry up before the meeting ends.

_____

9 You want another person to answer a question that has been directed at you.

_____

10 You want to conclude the meeting.

_____

2 The following extract is taken from a discussion at a meeting on business ethics. Put the missing phrases into each gap.

> If I understand you correctly
> That's a good point   could I just finish
> ~~I'd like to come in here~~
> I think Kate is better placed to answer that
> If I could just interrupt
> we should move on to the next item on the agenda

Dean John, I think you had a point to make about mis-selling.

John (0) Yes, I'd like to come in here. We have never had any written code of conduct for sales people; we have just assumed that …

Sarah (1) _____ , that's not true, actually. We do have the handbook …

John Sorry, Sarah, (2) _____ ? We have a selling handbook, but we don't have any code of ethical conduct for salespeople and I think that a lot of them don't really know what the boundaries are in persuading customers to sign a contract with us.

Dean (3) _____ , John. OK, I think we're all agreed on that now. Time is a little short and (4) _____ . That's the question of breach of confidence. Some customers have complained that we pass on information about them to other companies. Sarah, do you have a view on this?

Sarah Actually, (5) _____ . She's responsible for the customer database and marketing.

Kate Well, customers are always asked on the phone if they object to our giving their names to other companies for marketing purposes. If they are registering online then they have to tick a box to opt out of third-party marketing. Perhaps that is where the problem lies.

Dean (6) _____ , you're saying that an opt out may be unethical … that we should give them the chance to opt in, instead.

Kate No, that's not really what I meant. I think …

Reading Test: Part Four

Do Part Four of the Reading Test. Give yourself 10 minutes to complete the task.

PART FOUR
Questions 1–10

- Read this article about ethical investments.
- Choose the correct word to fill each gap **A, B, C** or **D**.
- There is an example at the beginning (**0**).

Ethical investing is just like any other type of investing, (**0**) *C* that the company that invests the money for the consumer (**1**) .... not to use that money to fund certain activities or behaviour that are believed to be harmful to the environment or to people. This may mean, for example, that a fund management company will not purchase shares in arms companies or firms that (**2**) .... harmful pesticides, or that a bank will not lend money to or otherwise (**3**) .... business for such companies.

Financial companies that practise ethical investment may not focus (**4**) .... such negative criteria, but positive criteria instead, meaning they will (**5**) .... out businesses that benefit the environment or the community. The range in policies is sometimes labelled by colour: a 'light green' company will (**6**) .... businesses whose actions or products are harmful to the environment, while a 'dark green' company will actively look for enviro-friendly or community-based businesses to invest in.

An increasingly common term for ethical investing is 'socially responsible investing', or SRI. SRI focuses on the positive (**7**) .... than the negative, and instead of blacklisting entire industries, it prefers to pick the company within the industry that is (**8**) .... the most to improve its business practices, and give that company encouragement in the form of investment. This positive reinforcement is seen as more likely to improve business practices (**9**) ....

It's important to remember that even though you may not directly invest your money – ie by buying shares – you may be indirectly investing it via a mortgage, pension or savings account, and by investing ethically you can have a (**10**) .... in what sort of activities your money supports.

0	A safe	B but	C except	D apart
1	A undertakes	B tells	C threatens	D engages
2	A set up	B develop	C innovate	D build
3	A nurture	B raise	C facilitate	D help
4	A about	B to	C on	D in
5	A see	B seek	C set	D research
6	A prevent	B deter	C miss	D avoid
7	A rather	B instead	C further	D increasingly
8	A doing	B making	C attempting	D taking
9	A commonly	B utterly	C throughout	D overall
10	A word	B say	C determination	D argument

9.1 Innovation

Describing products

1 Match each advertising slogan to the correct company.

> fast and efficient service
> innovative state-of the-art designs
> unbeatable value for money
> neat and compact solutions
> up-market designer labels at low prices
> ~~modern functional furniture~~
> reliable quality equipment

0 modern functional furniture

SPACE SAVING KITCHENS

1 _____

• RIOCH ARCHITECTS •

2 _____

3 _____

TQ CLOTHING COMPANY

4 _____

BETTAPRICE FOODS

5 _____

6 _____

2 What is the opposite of each of these adjectives?

0	practical	impractical
1	compact	b _____
2	modern	o _____
3	up-market	d _____
4	value for money	o _____
5	reliable	u _____
6	efficient	i _____

Pronunciation

3 In English the letter 'i' can be pronounced /aɪ/ as in *try* and or /ɪ/ as in *trip*. Put the words below into the right column in the table.

equipment	quick	time	image
private	finance	reliable	realise
finish	negative	client	limited
silent	efficient	simple	quality

/aɪ/	/ɪ/
time	quick

Collocations: verb + preposition

4 Complete the description of a product by putting the correct preposition in each gap.

The FX500 PVR is now (**0**) *on* sale (**1**) _____ most electrical stores or online. It consists (**2**) _____ two elements: a digital recorder and DVD player. It comes (**3**) _____ two colours, silver and black, and has a storage capacity of 320GB. Retailing (**4**) _____ just $200 it will appeal (**5**) _____ a first-time buyer rather than the specialist. One excellent feature is the standby saver, which runs (**6**) _____ rechargeable batteries and means that you don't waste electricity when the machine is on standby. Manufactured in Korea, it complies (**7**) _____ US and European standards and is compatible (**8**) _____ almost all makes of TV.

5 Write these expressions in the correct box according to which preposition comes before them.

the world   the same time   the market   home
a small scale   the pipeline   the end of the day
the end   the future   holiday   the face of it
least   practice   average   ~~the moment~~

at	in	on
the moment		

would

6 Complete each sentence using *would*, an appropriate verb and the words given in brackets.

0 If you could make it to the reception, *that would be great* (great).

1 In principle, _____ _____ (no problem).

2 If you could deliver direct, _____ _____ (easier for us).

3 _____ (your invitation), but I'm afraid I have another appointment.

4 _____ (your help), because I don't think I can do it on my own.

5 If I were in your shoes, _____ _____ (the same).

6 Before agreeing anything, _____ _____ (certain guarantees from you).

7 Make these statements from a negotiation sound more diplomatic by rephrasing them using *would*.

0 We need your help.
   We would appreciate your help.

1 Are you happy to give us a discount?

   _____

2 I will have to ask my boss about that.

   _____

3 That suits us OK too.

   _____

4 That's very difficult for us.

   _____

5 We can accept those terms.

   _____

6 In exchange, can you guarantee that …

   _____

Reading

8 Look at the article by a director of the World Innovation Council and complete the phrasal verbs by adding one of the pairs of prepositions.

up with	forward to	up to	up with
out for	out of	~~on with~~	

The importance of innovation

I have spent the last ten years trying to persuade European companies to (**0**) get *on with* the job of innovating and I am (**1**) running _____ _____ patience. Whenever I meet entrepreneurs and inventors, I ask them: 'What is the main obstacle to innovation that you face?' The answer I get in Europe is often the same: companies have cut back on investment because they don't feel the urgency to (**2**) come _____ _____ new ideas all the time. Why not? Because they are already in a dominant position. Of course, they (**3**) look _____ opportunities that might give them an advantage and they do take account of what is needed to (**4**) keep _____ developments in their sector, but in comparison with countries like India and China they don't invest heavily. These countries are (**5**) looking _____ a continuing economic boom. Innovation and scientific research is a key part of this. They know that to (**6**) stand _____ competition from other parts of the world, in the long run it will not be enough just to produce goods cheaply.

9 The two words in each pair below are similar in meaning. Answer the questions to explain the difference between them.

0 Which one uses a product or service and which one buys it?
a customer *buys a product*
a consumer *uses a product.*

1 Which one is general and which is specific?
competition _____
competitor _____

2 Which one means *to make something different* and which means *to make a contribution*?
to differentiate _____
to make a difference _____

3 Which one emphasises saving time and money and which one emphasises results?
effectiveness _____
efficiency _____

4 Which means *to reach the same level* and which means *to stay at the same level*?
catch up with _____
keep up with _____

5 Which means *to keep hold of* and which means *to keep up*?
to sustain _____
to retain _____

6 Both give you rights, but which one is like a copyright?
a patent _____
a licence _____

10 Complete each sentence by writing the verb in brackets as a noun or adjective.

0 The challenge is to develop an atmosphere that brings out employees' *creativity*. (create)

1 It's a very _____ product. (innovate)

2 There are leaders and _____ in the industry. (follow)

3 Business _____ is only possible with innovation. (grow)

4 Big _____ on research and development does not always produce big results. (spend)

5 Some good innovations have also been commercial _____ . (fail)

6 Competition is the _____ of innovation. (drive)

7 The idea is not only to win new customers but to retain _____ ones. (exist)

Negotiating

Reading

1 Read the article and decide whether the following statements are true (*T*) or false (*F*) according to the author. If the information is not given in the article write *D* 'doesn't say'.

1 Women prefer a win–win approach to negotiation. _____

2 A win-lose situation occurs when the emphasis is on the content not the relationship. _____

3 The win-lose approach is more likely to be adopted by men than women. _____

4 Negotiators who focus on building a relationship are looking primarily for a fair result. _____

5 Some people will make concessions just to keep on good terms. _____

In a negotiation, the two parties usually have two concerns. One is about the substance of the negotiation and one is about the nature of the relationship between the negotiating parties.

When a high degree of concern is expressed for the substance of the negotiation and a low degree of concern is expressed for the relationship of the parties, a 'Defeat' behaviour pattern is produced. This pattern is characterised by win-lose competition, pressure, intimidation, adversarial relationships and the negotiator attempting to get as much as possible for him / her. Defeating the other party at any cost becomes the negotiator's goal.

Interestingly, research shows that males favour the 'Defeat' approach more than females. A testosterone-induced negotiating style perhaps?

When the focus is building a compatible relationship in the hope that the negotiation will be successful, an 'Accommodate' behaviour pattern is produced. This pattern is characterised by efforts to promote harmony, avoidance of substantive differences, yielding to pressure to preserve the relationship and placing interpersonal relationships above the fairness of the outcome.

2 Complete the dialogue using phrases A–I.

> A would that be acceptable
> B would you be willing to   C in principle
> D our position is this
> E that's out of the question
> F what did you have in mind
> G Could we meet you half-way   H in return
> I ~~Thanks for agreeing to meet me.~~

A (0) I.

B It's a pleasure. So, tell me what you are looking for.

A (1) _____ . We have a great product, but no expertise in bringing products to market.

B And if I agree to help you with the marketing …?

A (2) _____ , we can offer a percentage of profits.

B I see. I would also need a fee for my time; not necessarily the full rate, but something.

A OK, but (3) _____ defer payment for six months?

B No, I couldn't really do that.

A (4) _____ ? A quarter up front, a quarter after three months and the balance after six months.

B I'd have to think about that.

A But, (5) _____ , you would consider it?

B Yes, I'm sure we can find some middle ground. As to the percentage, what are you offering?

A Five percent. (6) _____ ?

B That's a lot less than I imagined.

A Oh. (7) _____ ?

B More like 25%.

A I'm sorry. (8) _____ .

3 Match each expression with its definition.

0 spiral out of control	A begin all over again
1 a stumbling block	B escalate too quickly
2 go pear-shaped	C initial difficulties
3 teething problems	D compromise
4 see it through	E without any problems
5 find some middle ground	F an obstacle to agreement
6 plain sailing	G follow something to its conclusion
7 start from scratch	H go badly wrong

Reading and Listening Tests: Part Three

The approach to Part Three of the Reading Test and the Listening Test is similar: look or listen for key words to direct you to the relevant part of the passage and then choose an answer which is a paraphrase of what is said in the text.

PART THREE

- Read the article about 'innovation in the car industry' and answer the questions.
- For each question (**1–6**), choose the best answer (**A**, **B**, **C** or **D**).

Bosch warns on innovation risk-aversion

Europe's car industry is endangering its main selling point by being reluctant to commit money early enough to new technological innovations, according to the head of the world's largest parts supplier. Bernd Bohr, head of Bosch Auto, the privately-held German group that had $36bn in automotive sales last year, told the Financial Times that suppliers were having to accept more and more of the financial risk for developing new products. 'The risk for suppliers is higher and the payback time is longer,' Mr Bohr said. This could lead to a danger that innovations such as ABS brakes and ESP stability control systems may not be developed in the future. 'There is a danger that the European car industry loses speed on technology, and this is the selling point of the industry …' His outspoken comments underline the depth of feeling at the German group, because Bosch is known for being extremely careful in its public statements.

Franz Fehrenbach, Bosch's chief executive, told the FT last year that if it was a company listed on the stock market, it may not have accepted the initial high losses when developing diesel pumps – which went on to become one of the most successful products in the company's 131-year history. Mr Bohr said that developing a product these days took an average of about eight years from developing the initial platform to selling the product. Bosch, which invests about 10% of its revenues in research and development, could afford to take a more long-term approach than many suppliers, but Mr Bohr was clear that it had its limits and car-makers needed to be more proactive. He said two possible solutions were to introduce new innovations – which recently include parking-assistance systems – through a whole fleet of cars rather than just in the highest-priced vehicles. Also, suppliers and manufacturers should decide on standards for new technologies much earlier to avoid costly competition.

Mr Bohr said Bosch was expecting a better year than the 'difficult' 2006, with some growth in Europe, a decline in the US and booming business in India and China. Although Bosch is facing difficulties from low-cost competitors in some areas such as starters, generators and basic brakes, it also benefits from having a large local presence in China and India.

---

1 The author implies that the car industry's main selling point is
   A technological innovations.
   B new safety features.
   C greater fuel economy.
   D quality of its supplier partners.

2 The problem for suppliers funding innovation is that
   A there is no guarantee of success.
   B technology moves too quickly.
   C the return on investment is very slow.
   D the competition is too great.

3 The public statement from Bosch was unusual because
   A it implied criticism of other German carmakers.
   B it was more extreme than was expected.
   C they don't usually announce their views so strongly.
   D it went deeper into the problem than is normal.

4 Not being listed on the Stock exchange means that Bosch
   A finds it difficult to raise funds for development.
   B can more easily take risks with its investments.
   C can invest about 10% of its revenue in R&D.
   D has a better relationship with its suppliers.

5 The cost of new technologies can be kept down if
   A they are targeted at only a limited range of cars.
   B they are paid for by people who buy expensive cars.
   C suppliers and manufacturers share the cost of development.
   D the norms for each technology are agreed as soon as possible.

6 Bosch sales are
   A up in Europe, the US and China and India.
   B down in Europe and the US, up in China and India.
   C flat in Europe, down in the US, up in China and India.
   D up in Europe, China and India, down in the US.

Reading

1 Read the interviews with two executives about business travel. Match the statements to the right person, Amy Nauiokas or Tony Book or both.

0 doesn't use public transport   Tony

1 prefers to travel business class   _____

2 has a strategy for avoiding jet lag (tiredness) _____

3 chooses hotels that are small and cosy   _____

4 is cost-conscious when travelling   _____

5 tries to use non-polluting forms of transport _____

6 likes to stay in central hotels   _____

7 finds business people in the UK less direct   _____

8 makes their own travel arrangements   _____

American Amy Nauiokas is the managing director of Barclays Wealth, the dedicated stockbroking arm of the Barclays Bank Group. She travels around the UK and to the US and Asia on business.

'I have a budget and I book my travel direct. I do quite a lot of long-haul travel, so I have a certain routine worked out. I keep awake if the goal is to sleep when I arrive and I go to sleep if I need to work when I get off the flight. Often when I'm coming back from New York I'll get the last flight, sleep on the plane, arrive at 6 am and go into the office. I'm quite lucky because I can sleep anywhere. Also luckily, when I go long-haul, the company pays for me to travel business class.'

'I think the UK rail system is much better than the one in the US; mind you I'm not so sure about London underground. The New York subway is much more reliable, it would never just stop between stations for no apparent reason.'

'I like small, boutique-style hotels. My strategy is to find a home away from home and my home is more like a small property than one of these giant hotels. In New York, I recommend the Mercer in Soho. I still think the fun place to do business is New York; I just thrive on the pace and style of it. I don't think you can find a business culture that is more direct. In England, everyone is very pleasant, but it takes me a bit longer to find out when there are problems.'

Renewable energy entrepreneur Tony Book shuns the type of big cars usually associated with managing directors and instead drives up to 30,000 miles a year in a Toyota Prius, the hybrid car which uses a battery and petrol.

'Public transport is so bad. At least in the hybrid car I'm getting up to 600 miles on a tank of petrol. We should all be aware of the environment and my pet hate is those big 4X4s.'

Tony Book is the MD of Riomay, one of the country's leading suppliers of water heating and solar panels. He travels around the UK and the world, particularly to the Far East, on business. He flies a lot though, which is bad for the environment.

'I always go for the cheapest flight, which I book myself, and have no real preferences for particular airlines. I don't travel business class because I can't really see the point. You don't arrive any quicker or fresher. When you've got your own company and it's coming out of your pocket, you take a different view. Mind you, I'll look for upgrades if I can get them.'

'When looking for a hotel, I want value for money, comfort and, if I'm staying in a city, somewhere in a downtown location. I look on the Internet and book hotel rooms after seeing a virtual tour of the place, but I don't have any favourites or recommendations. I stay as high up as possible to get a good view of a city, smog permitting. I love visiting Japan. It's a land of contrasts: teeming millions in the cities, but in the country, it's incredibly beautiful.'

Future forms

2 Three people are sitting in a restaurant. None of them has been served yet. A fourth person arrives and asks them: 'What are you going to eat?' Each one describes his / her choice, but using a different future form. Explain why. (Think about: the timing of the decision, the menu, the waiter.)

A Ummmm ... I think I'll have the steak.

B I'm going to have the lobster.

C I'm just having some soup.

3 The CEO of a manufacturing company is discussing his schedule with his private secretary. Complete the dialogue by writing the verb in brackets in the correct future form.

S So, just to run through your diary for next Monday. You (**0**) *are having* (have) a working breakfast with the board from 8 to 9.30am. Then there (**1**) _____ (be) a conference call with the heads of the four subsidiaries scheduled for 10am. You (**2**) _____ (meet) the Minister for Industry for lunch at the Carlton at 1pm. What (**3**) _____ (you / say) to him, by the way?

CEO I (**4**) _____ (tell) him that unless the government (**5**) _____ (give) financial support for a new factory in the north-east, we (**6**) _____ (have) to look for sites outside the UK.

S He (**7**) _____ (not / like) that.

CEO Maybe not, but that's the reality. What (**8**) _____ (happen) in the afternoon?

S You (**9**) _____ (host) a question and answer session at the London Business School at 3pm.

CEO Who (**10**) _____ (be) there?

S The audience is mostly MBA students and on the panel there (**11**) _____ (be) two other CEO's, Dave Gardner and Joanna Browne.

CEO Oh, good, I like Joanna. When (**12**) _____ (it / end)? I was hoping to get some work done at some point!

S By 4.30pm. Your car (**13**) _____ (bring) you back here afterwards.

CEO And you haven't made any arrangements for the evening?

S No.

CEO Good, I (**14**) _____ (try) not to get home too late.

Events management

4 In the following dialogues people are discussing arrangements for events. Choose the best words to complete each dialogue.

1

A When our one millionth customer walks through the door, we'd like to (**0**) *remember /* *commemorate /* *memorise* the occasion with a special presentation.

B That's a good idea, but we need to get good (**1**) *advertising / publicity / advertisement* from it. I don't think the shop itself is a great (**2**) *site / premises / venue* for a presentation ceremony. It could (**3**) *reflect / look / return* badly on us.

A Nonsense. We can (**4**) *put up / put on / put off* a good show here without having to change too much around.

B And what's the prize going to be?

A I thought we could have a little (**5**) *reward / gratitude / award* ceremony with the winner getting a year's free groceries.

2

A I am very conscious of the fact that since the merger we haven't had any real social event for the two teams to (**1**) *go / become / get* to know each other better.

B No, you're right. It would be good to break the (**2**) *ice / barriers / frost* a bit.

A Yes, and also to give them a bit of a (**3**) *favour / treat / pleasure*. Everyone has been working incredibly hard over the last four months.

B What did you have in mind?

A Drinks and a meal, perhaps a bit of cabaret. Could you get a rough (**4**) *valuation / estimate / calculate* of what that would cost and get back to me?

B Sure. How many do you think would (**5**) *turn out / turn in / turn up*? 50? 60?

go and get

5 Decide whether these phrases are used with *go* or *get* and write them in the correct column.

> ~~ready~~   to know someone   ~~wrong~~   married
> missing   lost   crazy   tired   bankrupt
> people involved   to plan   over budget   started
> quiet   shopping

go	get
wrong	ready

6 Choose eight of the phrases from exercise 5 and make sentences with them.

I need to get ready for the meeting. It starts in five minutes.

Pronunciation

7 Read the information in the box then put the invisible linking consonants into these phrases.

> **Linking consonants**
> * Often, in English, words that begin with a vowel are linked to the consonant at the end of the word before.
>   *get over it* ➜ ge‿tove‿rit
> * If the preceding word ends with a vowel, an 'invisible' consonant is put in.
>   *go into it* ➜ go‿w‿into‿w‿it
>   *I am open to ideas* ➜ I‿y‿a‿mopen to‿w‿ideas

0 She expects to arrive at 4pm.
   She‿y‿expects to‿w‿arrive at 4pm.

1 The opening will be at 8am.
   _____

2 We didn't go out to a restaurant.
   _____

3 I am interested, if you are.
   _____

4 Can we just go over the agenda?
   _____

5 Do you ever lie about your age?
   _____

10.2 The language of proposals

The following answer to an exam question is well-organised, has few mistakes and addresses each point in the question. However, it was considered unsatisfactory as a piece of business communication because:
- it was too vague (no specific details or examples);
- it didn't make concrete recommendations.

1 Read the exam question and the answer. Underline the parts of the answer that seem too vague and non-specific.

2 Now improve the answer by adding more specific points in the places you have indicated.

Question 1
- You feel your company's main product or service would benefit from better publicity. The directors have asked you to write a proposal putting forward our ideas.
- Write your **proposal** for the directors:
  - mentioning the product or service concerned
  - stating the shortcomings of the current advertising
  - outlining how your competitors promote their products or services
  - suggesting a different approach to advertising.

To: The directors

    I would like to draw your attention to the performance of one of our main products, the energy drink, Zap.

    Unfortunately, it has experienced some problems in the market, while our competitors' products have improved their sales by an average of 8%. We need to take steps urgently to deal with this situation.

    The main problem is our advertising campaign, not the product. We need to find a different way to advertise the product or our product will continue to lose market share to its competitors.

    By contrast, they have used innovative styles of marketing and advertising, both on TV and radio and in magazines. In this way, they have attracted a lot of attention and gained new customers. We must do the same, because customers are bored of our advertising.

    My recommendations are as follows:
    – we should employ the services of specialists in the field of advertising to help us define a new campaign.
    – we should design some advertisements which feel fresh and attractive and run these on different types of advertising media: TV, radio, magazines, billboards etc.
    – we should use some famous people in the advertisements, because this will help to persuade consumers that it is a good product.

    Please consider these proposals carefully and do not hesitate to contact me for further details.

1 Read the prompt card that was given to the candidates in Part Three of the Speaking Test. Make a list of ideas for reducing spending and convincing staff to adopt these ideas.

Business travel

Your company is based in the USA, but has subsidiaries in Europe and China. It sells its products all around the world. Travel is an important part of its activity. However spending on business travel is too high and you would like to reduce it.

Discuss, and decide together:
• how you could reduce spending on travel
• how you can persuade the staff that such savings are necessary.

---

travelling economy class

_____

_____

_____

_____

_____

point out that reducing travel is environmentally friendly

_____

_____

2 Look at the transcript of the discussion between two candidates. Improve or correct the underlined phrases.

A So, (**0**) <u>we must discuss the topic</u> of spending on travel. (**1**) <u>What opinion do you have about</u> this question?

  0 *we need to look urgently at the problem*

  1 _____

B (**2**) <u>In my thinking</u>, (**3**) <u>most important</u> is to stop people flying business class. Maybe for the senior directors it is sometimes necessary, because they need to arrive for a meeting feeling fresh after a long flight. (**4**) <u>On another hand</u>, for more junior staff or for short journeys, it is just a waste of money.

  2 _____

  3 _____

  4 _____

A (**5**) <u>I am agree with you.</u> (**6**) <u>It is another true</u> that if we used only one airline for all the flights, we could get a better deal from them. They would give us a better price and (**7**) <u>more</u> perhaps also allow us to participate in some kind of loyalty scheme.

  5 _____

  6 _____

  7 _____

B (**8**) <u>I like.</u> We could do the same thing with car hire. If we launch a call for tender for all the car hire worldwide and then choose the lowest bidder, we are sure to make savings.

  8 _____

A So, (**9**) <u>if I can do a summary of these points</u>, we (**10**) <u>agreed</u> that we should look first at air travel …

  9 _____

  10 _____

3 Think of three or four follow-on questions that the examiner might ask.

Do you think that with modern telecommunications, business people don't really need to travel at all?

11.1 The economy

Economic issues

1 Read the text about a speech given by Hillary Clinton on the US economy in April 2007 and answer the following questions. What point did she make about ...

- the level of ordinary working people's pay?
- the effects of the country's debts?
- the cost of medical treatment?
- the foundations of the American economy?

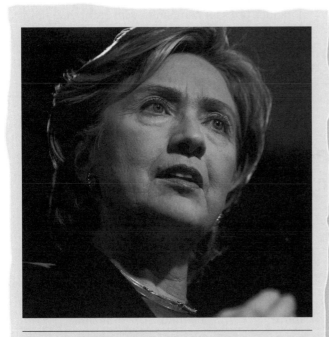

In a speech to Chicago's business leaders, Hillary Clinton observed that in the current economic climate, wages have stagnated while company profits have soared; that the budget deficit is threatening future innovation; that health care costs have become too much of a burden for the middle class.

It was Mrs Clinton's remarks on the middle class, and on the working poor, that drew the most applause. 'America did not build the greatest economy in the world because we had rich people,' she said. 'Nearly any society has some of those. We built the greatest economy in the world because we built the American middle class. We can't be secure without a strong economy, and we cannot sustain our deepest values without an economy that rewards hard work.'

2 Cross out the word that doesn't collocate with the word in bold.

- 0 **economy**: depressed / ~~heavy~~ / stagnant
- 00 **unemployment**: rate / benefit / ~~credit~~
- 1 **living**: cost of / standard of / quality of
- 2 **economy**: blooming / booming / buoyant
- 3 **sector**: private / civil / public
- 4 **market**: job / labour / work
- 5 **trade**: excess / deficit / surplus
- 6 **tax**: burden / bill / load
- 7 **consumer**: faith / confidence / spending
- 8 **government**: present / subsidy / grant
- 9 **power**: consuming / buying / purchasing

3 Match the words A–G, ending *-less*, to the correct definitions 1–6.

0 having no idea	A homeless
1 nowhere to live	B speechless
2 of no value	C clueless
3 Unemployed	D worthless
4 unable to reply	E penniless
5 showing no pity	F ruthless
6 in complete poverty	G jobless

4 Match the prefixes on the left with A–I to make words.

0 under	A fidence
1 re	B courage
2 en	C petition
3 de	D locate
4 dis	E employment
5 com	F mine
6 con	G efficiency
7 in	H pressed
8 un	I abled

Conditionals (types 1 and 2)

> **Remember!**
>
> **Type 1** *If* + present, ... *will* + infinitive = real and possible
>
> **Type 2** *If* + past, ... *would* + infinitive = unreal or improbable

5 Use type 1 or 2 conditionals to complete the sentences, using the verbs in brackets.

0 If I *were* (be) you, I *would be* (be) very careful.

1 If you _____ (not / mind),
I _____ (leave) a little early to catch my train.

2 If the exchange rate _____ (be) better, we _____ (do) a lot more business with them.

3 I _____ (not / have) any supper, if it _____ (be) OK with you. I had a big lunch.

4 She _____ (find) people more helpful, if she _____ (be / not) so rude.

5 If the government really _____ (want) people to use their cars less, it _____ (triple) the price of petrol.

6 I _____ (take) the job if I _____ (think) I had the right skills.

7 Do you think that he _____ (mind) if I _____ (borrow) his car?

6 Use an *if*-clause to explain why you would do the following:

0 miss a day's work   *If I felt really unwell*

1 go into work when you were sick

_____

2 accept a gift from a client

_____

3 refuse a job promotion

_____

4 retire early

_____

5 walk out of a meeting

_____

6 interrupt in the middle of a presentation

_____

7 Look at these proposed government measures and use type 1 conditionals to say what is the probable consequence of each one.

The government is planning to:

0 introduce a road charging scheme for cars in big cities
This will reduce traffic congestion.

1 give working women extra money to pay for the cost of child care _____

2 reduce the level of benefit payments to the unemployed _____

3 increase income tax for top earners from 40% to 60% _____

4 reduce taxes for companies with fewer than ten employees _____

5 provide every primary school with a computer room _____

6 subsidize rail transport for commuters

_____

Pronunciation

8 English has a lot of vowel sounds, both long and short. One common mistake for learners of English is to shorten the long ones. Decide if the following words contain a long or short vowel sound and complete the table.

laid	food	slip
said	good	sleep
above	medium	include
move	medical	pudding
cloth	range	client
both	rang	clinic

long vowels	short vowels

9 Check your answers to exercise 8, then say the words aloud. If you exaggerate the length or shortness of each vowel, you will come close to the natural sound.

Relocation experiences

10 Read the description of a relocation advice service and complete it by writing one of the words from the box in each gap.

> grants   exempt   outgoing   premises   rental   ~~authority~~   property   move   estate

Derbyshire relocation services

We are a team funded by Derbyshire local (0) *authority* that provides business relocation services for both incoming and (1) _____ company personnel. Our packages include a wide range of services such as:

- orientation around the area

- assistance with finding business (2) _____ and moving house (purchase or (3) _____)

- help obtaining local government (4) _____

- advice on local schools.

We work with local commercial and residential (5) _____ agents, whether for buying or selling your (6) _____ . Our services have been designed for employees who are moving within the UK, but also for their company's own HR staff. Our aim is to help our clients (7) _____ as smoothly as possible. Our services are not free but are (8) _____ from tax.

11 Match each of the expressions 1–8 with a phrase that means the same from A–I.

0 stress-free	A relaxed
1 laid-back	B convenient
2 a carrot	C go for it
3 handy	D an opportunity not to be missed
4 have it both ways	E an incentive
5 too good to pass up	F be there at the beginning
6 give it a second thought	G without hassle
7 take the plunge	H enjoy the benefits with no disadvantages
8 get in on the ground floor	I consider before acting

12 Complete the sentences with the correct preposition.

0 I have a good working relationship *with* her.

1 It is a relationship based _____ trust.

2 She showed a lot of interest _____ our products.

3 He has a reputation _____ being a tough negotiator.

4 He has access _____ some excellent contacts in the Trade Ministry.

5 Chinese people love eating _____ at restaurants.

6 Don't worry _____ the time it takes to build a relationship.

7 You should find _____ if you qualify _____ a government grant.

8 She has invested heavily _____ the company in the last five years.

9 They have spent a lot of money _____ new equipment.

Remember!

- Be organised
- Be to the point
- Be appropriate

1 Complete this proposal using linking words or phrases to make it flow more naturally. Use some of the words in the box.

> on the other   unfortunately   as I see it   so
> also   on the one hand   although   moreover
> first of all   for example   indeed

PROPOSAL TO REVIEW MARKETING STRATEGY

This proposal sets out to analyse our current marketing strategy and (**0**) *also* to make recommendations on how it could be improved.

(**1**) _____ , a little background. In July 2006 it was decided to move away from mass market advertising and follow a policy of targeted marketing. (**2**) _____ , for trade painters and decorators we ran a campaign by advertising in trade journals and using point-of-sale presentation stands.

(**3**) _____ , after one year, sales in this sector were only 3% better than before. (**4**) _____ , sales in the mass market sector fell by 4%.

(**5**) _____ , what is the best course of action now? (**6**) _____ , we have two possibilities.

(**7**) _____ we could go back to our original policy of mass market advertising or, alternatively, we could develop a new strategy focusing more on the product itself than the advertising.

(**8**) _____ this might take longer, I think it would get to the root of the problem.

2 Make these sentences from a report more concise by removing unnecessary words.

0   The aim of this report, and the purpose for it, is to evaluate, through careful examination, the current situation with our repair service offered for faulty goods.
   The aim of this report is to evaluate our repair service for faulty goods.

1   In terms of price for a top of the range hairdryer, we consider that $150 is much too expensive for people to afford.

2   To sum up, I would like to conclude by saying that of the two options presented above, my preference would be to choose the second option since it represents a more cost-effective solution, and money is clearly an important consideration.

3 Put the underlined phrases in an internal email into a less formal style.

Dear Jim

I hope you are well. I (**0**) <u>apologise for</u> *I'm sorry about* the long delay in replying to your email.
(**1**) <u>However</u>, I wanted to research your question thoroughly before (**2**) <u>providing you with an answer</u>.

You (**3**) <u>enquired whether</u> it was possible to extend the life of our standard mobile phone battery, (**4**) <u>since</u> you have received a (**5**) <u>significant number</u> of complaints about it. The answer is 'yes', but the solution may be expensive. We source our batteries from a Korean supplier which manufactures three different grades of battery. The ones (**6**) <u>which we purchase</u> are the cheapest in the range. (**7**) <u>It will come as no surprise that</u> they also have the shortest life.

If you (**8**) <u>wish</u> me to send you more technical details, (**9**) <u>please do not hesitate to</u> ask me.

11.3 Speaking Test: Part Two

1 Look at the topic below, chosen by a candidate in the speaking test, and the transcript of the presentation and discussion. Correct the mistakes the candidates made, using the examiner's notes.

Time Management
The importance of:
- organising your time efficiently
- prioritising tasks

2 Imagine you are the examiner. Write two questions that you would like to ask the candidates about what they have said.

Do you think you manage your time effectively?

_____

_____

_____

0 singular / plural	**Christine** So I'd like to say (**0**) ~~some~~ *a* few words about time management.
1 tense	A lot of people (**1**) are finding it very difficult to organise their time efficiently and I think that there are two simple rules you can follow that will help you.
2 verb form 3 modal verb	The first thing I recommend is planning and (**2**) make lists of the things that you (**3**) must to do each day and then look at the list and see what is manageable and what is not.
4 preposition	Secondly it's very important to prioritise the things (**4**) at your list to be sure that you are getting the important things done first. I
5 adverb / adjective	think that a lot of people go first to the things that are (**5**) easily to do rather than those which are really important and need doing.
6 tense	I think (**6**) I mentioned the main points. Do you have any questions Andrea?
7 gerund / infinitive 8 missing word 9 vocabulary 10 gerund / infinitive	**Andrea** Yes, I agree with you about the need (**7**) of prioritising. There is just one point I (**8**) would to add which is that if you (**9**) do long lists of the things you have to do it can be quite alarming and the temptation is (**10**) doing the things which are quickest to do, so that you cross off the most items.
11 modal verb 12 preposition 13 word order	**Christine** Yes, that's right. You (**11**) must probably put a time next to each item according (**12**) on how long it's going to take. Or (**13**) even you can have two lists, one of short-term goals and one of long-term goals.

Globalisation

1 **In the context of globalisation, think of a word that goes with each of the following.**

0 merging *cultures*

1 _____ village

2 multinational _____

3 _____ barriers

4 cheap _____

5 _____ movement of capital

6 global _____

7 _____ countries

8 deregulated _____

2 **Read the quotations in the speech bubbles and say who thinks globalisation:**

0 is beneficial only for well-off people in developed countries.   *Jimmy Carter*

1 should be about more than just investing where you want to.   _____

2 will only be considered a success if it makes people better off in the long term.   _____

3 means that the free market determines the direction of world politics.   _____

4 means that companies can recruit better people.   _____

5 is just another term for expansion of American power.   _____

6 is good for the consumer.   _____

'Globalisation and free trade do spur economic growth, and they lead to lower prices on many goods.' Robert Reich

'If you're totally illiterate and living on one dollar a day, the benefits of globalisation never come to you.' Jimmy Carter

The regime of globalisation promotes an unfettered marketplace as the dynamic instrument organising international relations.' William Greider

'Globalisation presumes sustained economic growth. Otherwise, the process loses its economic benefits and political support.' Paul Samuelson

'Globalisation has changed us into a company that searches the world, not just to sell or to source, but to find intellectual capital – the world's best talents and greatest ideas.' Jack Welch

'There is a growing consensus that globalisation must now be reshaped to reflect values broader than simply the freedom of capital.' John J Sweeney

'For when we talk about the spreading power and influence of globalisation, aren't we really referring to the spreading economic and military might of the US?' Fredric Jameson

Speculation

3 Complete this table of verb forms used to speculate about the past. Then write an example sentence for each form.

wish + _____

should + _____ + past participle

If + past perfect, _____ + *have* + past participle

could / *might* + *have* + _____

4 Write the following in order, from 99% certainty that it <u>was</u> the case to 99% certainty that it <u>wasn't</u>.

It might have been John who told them.
It must have been John who told them.
It can't have been John who told them.
It could have been John who told them.
It may have been John who told them.

_____ 99% **YES**
_____ 50%
_____ 50%
_____ 50%
_____ 99% **NO**

5 Write the correct form of the verb in brackets to complete each of these sentences.

0 I wish I *had known* (know) that before I spoke to her.

1 If I _____ (feel) more confident, I would have taken the risk.

2 You should _____ (ask) me. I would have said 'yes.'

3 If you had lost it, I _____ (be) furious.

4 I wish that I _____ (not / mention) that I was looking for another job.

5 I don't know why he's so late. I suppose he might _____ (forget).

6 I don't think anyone could _____ (predict) that this would happen.

6 Look at each situation and then complete the sentence speculating about it.

0 The management didn't really listen and so employees voted to strike.
The result might *have been different if the management had listened.* (be different if …)

1 They were in such a hurry to launch the new product that they didn't test it properly for faults.
They wished _____ (do more tests)

2 They advertised the job internally and only got two applicants.
They could _____ (get a better response if …)

3 He made the decision independently and then was surprised when everyone felt ignored.
He should _____ (consult more people)

4 She found that without a university education, her career progress was limited.
She wished _____ (go to university)

5 She sold her shares in France Telecom two months before the stock market crash.
If she _____ (keep her shares)

6 Both sides maintained their position and no agreement was reached.
If either side _____ (make a compromise)

7 They offered me a job and I refused. Since then the company has been incredibly successful.
I should _____ (take the job)

8 They went bankrupt because they failed to invest when they needed to.
They could _____ (avoid bankruptcy if …)

7 Decide whether the letter 'g' in the following words is pronounced as a hard or soft sound; for example, *got* = hard 'g', *German* = soft 'g'. Complete the table.

merge manager gentleman target colleague angel gesture region angle margin guest legal global

hard 'g'	soft 'g'
	merge

Cross-cultural communication

8 Write down two suggestions for the following:

0 things you can present to a business partner you are visiting

a small gift OR your business card

1 ways to dress for a business meeting

_____

2 gestures used to greet someone you meet

_____

3 ways to address your business partner

_____

4 ways of talking to your business guest to make them feel relaxed.

_____

9 Read the passage and say what you think the ultimate gesture is.

The Ultimate Gesture

According to Roger G. Axtell, the 'ultimate gesture' carries certain welcome characteristics unlike any other single gesture.

First, this 'ultimate gesture' is known everywhere in the world. It is absolutely universal.

Second, it is rarely, if ever, misunderstood. Primitive tribes and world leaders alike know and use this gesture.

Third, scientists believe this particular gesture actually produces a beneficial physiological effect.

Fourth, as you travel around the world, this gesture may help you get out of the most difficult situations.

What is this singular signal, this miracle mien, this giant of all gestures?

10 Complete these sentences on behaviour in different countries by adding one word in each gap. The first letter has been given for you.

Body language around the world

China
The western custom of (**0**) shaking hands is the customary form of greeting, but often a
(**1**) n _____ of the head is sufficient

Far East
One thing all far eastern cultures have in
(**2**) c _____ is a tendency to avoid direct eye
(**3**) c _____ . Respect for authority and for one's elders is also a strong (**4**) f _____ of Asian culture. People in the Far East will also avoid
(**5**) l _____ face or bringing shame on their social group.

Japan
Japanese are very polite people and yawning or blowing your nose in public is considered
(**6**) r _____ .

Philippines
Filipinos may (**7**) g _____ one another with a quick lifting of the eyebrows.

Korea
Having first- (**8**) h _____ experience of Korean negotiating style is very important, because your style may prove more important than the price.

America
(**9**) A _____ of personal space is important. It is impolite to stand closer than 75 cm to someone.

12.2 Social English

Small talk

1 Match each of the expressions 0–8 with the phrase that is closest in meaning from A–I.

0 It's not important.	A Would you like a lift?
1 That would be great.	B Don't worry.
2 Can I help you?	C I don't want to put you out.
3 Please do.	D Can I give you a hand?
4 That is a nice offer.	E Do you mind if I ...?
5 You're welcome.	F That's very kind of you.
6 Please don't trouble yourself.	G Not at all.
7 Is it OK for me to ...?	H I'd love to.
8 Can I take you in my car?	I Go ahead.

2 Respond to each of these statements / questions with a short response

0 Hi, how are you?

Fine, thanks. And you?

1 How do you do? I'm Jane Moor.

_____

2 I'm so sorry to be late.

_____

3 Thank you for all your help.

_____

4 Lovely weather, isn't it?

_____

5 How was your trip?

_____

6 Can I give you a hand with that suitcase?

_____

7 You're looking well.

_____

8 Would you like to go for a drink after work?

_____

9 Can I just answer the phone?

_____

10 Do you mind if I smoke?

_____

3 Correct the underlined words in this conversation.

Qiu Qing Hello. I hope you (**0**) <u>didn't</u> haven't been waiting long.

Paul No. It's OK. I brought some work with me. How are you?

Qiu Qing I'm very (**1**) <u>fine</u> _____ , thank you. And you?

Paul Quite busy these days. But things are going well.

Qiu Qing I'm glad (**2**) <u>hearing</u> _____ that.

Paul Would you like a coffee?

Qiu Qing Yes. that (**3**) <u>is</u> _____ great. But I don't want to put you (**4**) <u>off</u> _____ .

Paul It's no trouble. But it's instant, I'm afraid.

Qiu Qing Don't (**5**) <u>be troubled</u> _____ . I prefer instant.

Paul Sorry, that's my phone ringing. Do you mind if I take the call?

Qiu Qing No, of course not. Please (**6**) <u>get forward</u> _____ . I'm not (**7**) <u>on</u> _____ a hurry.

Paul Sorry about that. So, what about the contract? Do you think Thompson will sign?

Qiu Qing Well, I hope (**8**) <u>it</u> _____ , but I am beginning to doubt (**9**) <u>so</u> _____ . I have another meeting with them next week.

Paul Is there anything I can do to help?

Qiu Qing That's kind (**10**) <u>to</u> _____ you, but I think it's easier for me to deal with the Chinese representative.

Paul Whatever you prefer.

I Do Part Five of the Reading Test. Give yourself 10 minutes to complete the task.

- Read this article about Iceland's energy resources.
- Write ONE word in each gap.
- There is an example at the beginning (**0**).

If there is a paradise for environmentalists, Iceland must be (**0**) ...it.... . It is the world's most energy efficient country, with 70% of its needs covered by domestically produced renewables. The volcanic island and (**1**) .... 300,000 inhabitants are blessed with natural hot springs. All (**2**) .... the island's electricity is produced cleanly – 84% through hydropower, while the rest comes from geothermal energy, using the heat from the earth.

Fossil fuels are used only for transport, but (**3**) .... here Iceland is determined to get rid of them completely. In 1998, the government decided to replace oil and gas (**4**) .... hydrogen as soon as possible. Three years ago, it opened the world's first hydrogen station and started a trial of three buses powered by hydrogen.

But it was (**5**) .... always like this. Iceland used to be a poor country that (**6**) .... to rely on imports of fossil fuels for everything. That (**7**) .... until the 1973 oil shock, when OPEC countries quadrupled prices. At that point Iceland started converting houses to geothermal heating, which is very cheap and costs less (**8**) .... fossil fuels.

There have been attempts to export Iceland's green riches abroad. Studies have been made on trying to send electricity through cables to Scotland, but (**9**) .... the moment it's not economical. If energy prices continue to go up and the price of the technology comes down, (**10**) .... something could be done about it. If exploited to the full, it is thought the energy could supply all of the electricity of a country the size of Scotland.

2 Do Part Six of the Reading Test. Give yourself 10 minutes to complete the task.

- In most of the lines there is one extra word. It is either grammatically incorrect or does not fit in with the sense of the text. Some lines, however, are correct.
- If a line is correct, write CORRECT next to it.
- If there is an extra word, write the extra word next to it.

0	Economic 'globalisation' is a historical and process, the result of	......and......
00	human innovation and technological progress. It refers to the increasing	CORRECT
1	integration of economies around the world, particularly through trade	....
2	and financial flows. The term sometimes can also refers to the movement of	....
3	people (labour) and knowledge (technology) across international borders.	....
4	There are also with broader cultural, political and environmental dimensions	....
5	to globalisation. At its most basic, there is not nothing mysterious about	....
6	globalisation. The term has come into common usage since the 1980s,	....
7	reflecting technological advances that have made it more easier and quicker	....
8	to complete international transactions – both trade and financial flows.	....
9	It refers on to an extension beyond national borders of the same market forces	....
10	that have been operated for centuries at all levels of human economic activity	....
11	– village markets, urban industries, or financial centres. Markets promote	....
12	efficiency by allowing people and economies to focus on that what they do best.	....

Answer key

MODULE 1

1.1

Working life

1
1 educated	2 left	3 applied
4 trained	5 set up	6 joined
7 graduated	8 worked	9 recruited
10 retired	11 moved	

2 1 unemployment   2 trainees (*people who receive training*)   3 recruitment   4 pay (= *salary; payment means a single instance eg 'please make your payment by credit card'*)   5 promotion   6 applications (*applicants are the people who apply*)   7 retirement   8 training

3 1 There's no point / It's useless + gerund   2 I plan / I aim + infinitive   3 I am thinking of / I am considering + gerund   4 I am prepared / I am happy + infinitive   5 I adore / I am keen on + gerund   6 I wasn't able / I failed + infinitive

4
1 I'm not used to **driving on the left**.
2 She is good at **managing people**.
3 I plan **to leave at the end of the year**.
4 Did you manage **to contact Jane**?
5 She is reluctant **to increase the prices**.
6 Did you have any difficulty **downloading the software**?
7 Does the job involve **speaking French**?
8 When do you expect **to arrive approximately**?
9 What do you think about **going to the cinema**?
10 Please avoid **calling between 10 and 12**.
11 The flights are full. Would you consider **taking the train**?
12 It's not worth **flying business class**.

5 In words of two syllables the stress falls on the first syllable if the word is a noun, on the second syllable if the word is a verb

6 **ba**ckground   sup**ply**   **con**tract   **stu**dent   pro**mote**   in**vol**ve   re**tain**   **coll**ege   att**end**   **sta**tus

7 pres**ent** verb   perm**it** verb   **ob**ject noun   **in**crease noun   **con**flict noun   **con**test noun   exp**ort** verb   ins**ult** verb

8
0 A (*we are looking for bright and capable young graduates*)
1 B (*independent and responsible*)
2 B (*regardless of the candidate's sex, religion or ethnic background*)
3 C (*Please supply character references*)
4 B (*masters degree, 10 years' nursing experience* etc.)
5 A (*No direct experience is necessary*)
6 C (*voted 'most dynamic newcomer'*)
7 A (*Excellent career prospects*)

1.2

Asking and answering questions

1
1 First of all, Dr Wolf, can you tell me why this price rise is necessary?
2 Obviously, it's not something we wanted to do. It has been forced on us by higher oil prices.
3 But you don't actually produce much of your electricity from burning oil, do you?
4 No, but the price of gas is linked to the price of oil and we do burn lot of gas.
5 But even if gas has gone up, how you can justify these prices when you have just announced record profits?
6 These new prices are necessary to protect our future profits, not our past profits.
7 Oh, I see. So you'll be making just as much money out of your customers this year, will you?
8 In fact, our profits this year will be used to fund a very expensive investment programme in our network.
9 And finally, do you know why other companies haven't increased their prices by the same amount?
10 I can't speak for others but I would be surprised if they didn't increase them in the near future.

2
1 Do you actually produce much of your electricity from burning oil?
2 Will you be making just as much money out of your customers this year?
3 Why haven't other companies increased their prices by the same amount?

3
1 You are quite inexperienced, aren't you?
2 How much sales experience do you have?
3 Do you think you have the necessary skills for the job?
4 You have done this kind of work before, have you?
5 Would you like a coffee?
6 You don't live in London, do you?
7 Why did you leave your last job?
8 Can you tell me why you find this job attractive?

1.3
Reading Test: Part One

1
- 0 D *(people entering the workforce are very poorly equipped to deal with the demands of working life)*
- 1 E *(we, the older generation, must accept that these are the values of today)*
- 2 A *(they think less about work and more about leisure time)*
- 3 C *(it doesn't necessarily follow that they are less committed to their jobs)*
- 4 E *(a fear of being poor)*
- 5 B *(Employees have much less loyalty to their employers these days)*
- 6 D *(when they are faced with the prospect of learning more on the job and serving their time to gain this necessary experience, they become frustrated)*
- 7 B *(they need this flexibility)*

MODULE 2

2.1
Growing the company

1
1 warehouse 2 subsidiary 3 plant
4 headquarters 5 division

2
British bank fears **take-over** by cash-rich Spanish giant
Car plant closes: 800 **laid off**
Keltel to **sell off** failing Internet business
BP and Shell **merge** to form world's largest oil company
Deanly shares will **go public** next year
Administrators called in as Lanco **goes bankrupt**
Chemico **expands** its European operations by buying Toxico

3

Verb	Noun
expand	expansion
develop	**development**
merge	**merger**
acquire	**acquisition**
grow	**growth**
innovate	innovation
solve	solution
classify	classification
evolve	evolution
tend	tendency

4
a) The stress always falls on the syllable before *-ion*.
b) In other words of three or more syllables the stress often falls on the third from last syllable.

5
bankruptcy evo**lu**tion di**vi**sion sub**si**diary **stra**tegy distri**bu**tion sig**ni**ficant compe**ti**tion com**pe**titive phi**lo**sophy

6

Present	Past	Past participle
begin	**began**	begun
become	became	**become**
lose	lost	**lost**
buy	**bought**	**bought**
put	**put**	put
rise	**rose**	risen
fall	fell	**fallen**
feel	**felt**	**felt**
spend	spent	**spent**
find	**found**	found
found	**founded**	**founded**

7 1 C 2 F 3 B 4 G 5 E 6 D

8
1 Even though revenue was down over the course of the year, our profit margins improved. ✓
2 In April we ~~had begun~~ work on a bus terminal in Shanghai. **began**
3 In Shanghai we used the same design that we ~~used to use~~ in Beijing a year earlier. **had used**
4 Because many existing projects were coming to an end, we made it a priority to look for new business. ✓ *(we could also say here 'had come to an end')*
5 In May, a new head of international business ~~has been~~ appointed. **was**
6 We found that we ~~wasted~~ a lot of time in the planning stages. **were wasting / had wasted**
7 The official opening was attended by the president of Iran. ✓
8 Our R & D department ~~was working~~ on a new high speed railway which will be launched next year. **has been working**

9

Employees — Stakeholders — eg Customers
Shareholders — — Suppliers
Local community

10
1 I am very **involved** in the development of new products.
2 Customers are generally very **satisfied** with the service they get. *(something is 'satisfactory', people are 'satisfied')*
3 We have a very **hierarchichal** structure, with about 15 levels from top to bottom
4 It's a very **innovative** company which empowers individuals.
5 I am consulted both on everyday matters and also on more **strategic** decisions.

11 6 At Google the emphasis is on **informality**.

7 Like most banks our culture is influenced by the amount of **bureaucracy**.

8 The most important thing for employees is to have **consistency**; not constant change.

9 In advertising, the main thing is to bring out employees' natural **creativity**.

10 **Recognition** can be financial or simply a few words of praise.

12 1 balance   2 reward   3 empowered
4 recognised   5 mutual   6 satisfaction
7 welfare   8 clear   9 retention

2.2
Presenting facts

1 0 D   1 E   2 I   3 A   4 H   5 F   6 C   7 B   8 G

2 1 to   2 as   3 if   4 until   5 by   6 in   7 has   8 the
9 up   10 my

3 1 ... to present **to** you our ... (OR ... to **present our** ...)

2 I'm going to describe **to** you the development ... (OR ... to **describe the** development ...)

3 And I'd like to **ask you** this question ...

4 Can anyone tell **me** why we ... (OR Can anyone **say** why we ...)

5 When I have explained the reasons **to** you ... (OR ... **explained the** reasons ...)

6 The next graph **shows you** how we ... (OR ... **shows** how we ...)

4 Students' own answers.

2.3
Speaking Test: Part One

1 1 **Actually**, it's German.

2 Yes but, **for me**, money is not the important thing.

3 **I don't see it that way**. I think it is a very risky strategy.

4 **On the whole**, that's true, but there are opportunities.

5 **Not really**. It tends to be less dynamic.

6 **I doubt it**. It's only a two-year contract.

7 **I agree**. It affects your whole career.

2 1 E   2 F   3 A   4 B   5 D

3 1 **Examiner** What does your job involve exactly?
Candidate I am responsible **for** searching the press **every day / each day** for articles about our company.

2 **Examiner** Will you continue to work there at the end of your apprenticeship?
Candidate Yes, I hope **so**. But maybe I **will have to** apply for a job with another company.

3 **Examiner** And what do you hope to be doing ten years from now?
Candidate My ambition is **to work** in the marketing field, because that is what I **specialise** in.

4 **Examiner** Do you think it's OK for pharmaceutical companies to advertise medicines?
Candidate It depends **on** what kind of product they are advertising. In my **view / opinion**, it's fine to advertise if you are honest about the benefits.

5 **Examiner** But perhaps that's not always the case?
Candidate I **agree** with you that some companies overstate benefits, but **on the whole** they are very responsible.

MODULE 3
3.1
Communication at work

1 1 receiving   2 issuing / putting out   3 attending
4 taking   5 makes / gives   6 produce / publish
7 putting / posting   8 running / launching
9 circulating / sending out

2

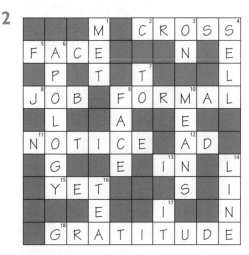

3 1 I **do** apologise for the delay.

2 If you **would** be kind enough to give me your mobile number, I'll call you back in a few minutes.

3 I **do** understand your worries.

4 **Would** 9am be a convenient time?

5 I**'ll** get back to you as soon as I can.

6 **Can** I be of any more assistance?

7 You **may** call me on this number whenever you like.

5 1 G 2 F 3 H 4 B 5 E 6 A 7 D

6 1 promise and undertake **to do something**
2 urge and encourage **someone to do something**
3 suggest and propose **doing** or **that someone do something**
4 persuade and convince **someone to do something**
5 dissuade and discourage **someone from doing something**
6 ask and invite **someone to do something**
7 criticise and blame **someone for doing something**

7 1 The Finance Minister promised **to simplify the tax system and to reduce the burden of tax on companies**.
2 The Chairman urged **investors to be patient** …
3 A source close to the management suggested **relaunching the product in a year or so**.
4 Hamilton praised **his team for working hard** …
5 Fredericks denied **showing favouritism to his son** …
6 The industry watchdog criticised **Degas for putting unfair pressure on customers.**
7 The spokeswoman discouraged **consumers from buying dairy products from France until more was known about the disease.**
8 The head of the airline threatened **to drop prices too, if the competition dropped theirs** …

8 0 C (*even though the media world may be fragmenting, there still seems to be a fundamental connection between people and products*)
1 E (*demands a shift in the way that brands and businesses try to get their message across*)
2 C (*A brand that can successfully open up to its critics and, crucially, get them involved in creating a better product, can soon find itself with some key supporters in the online world*)
3 B (*the threat posed to companies by individual consumers, who suddenly have a voice which they can use to complain about a particular product or service*)
4 A (*but the business world has struggled to come to terms with the increase of user-generated content*)
5 D (*we are moving from an age of channel media – where infrastructure and content and distribution is owned by organisations – to one where everybody can play a part*)
6 A (*the huge size of online communities such as MySpace has already brought Google and Yahoo! into these sites*)
7 E (*bloggers detest intrusive marketing in their personal space online*)
8 D (*that does not mean those organisations go away*)

3.2
Email exchange

1 Dear Didier
(**0**) Thanks for offering to (**1**) **help** me with the Blane report. The chairman specifically (**2**) **suggested that I** compile it and (**3**) **so** I (**4**) **don't** feel I (**5**) **can** accept your kind offer. (**6**) **But** (**7**) **please** send me any relevant information that might help me with it. (**8**) **Do** call me if you (**9**) **would like** to discuss it (**10**) **more**.
Kind regards
Jean

2 Dear Ms Doyle
(**0**) Thank you for your email. (**1**) **I apologise** for the delay in sending you the T-shirt that you ordered.
(**2**) **Currently**, we (**3**) **do not** have the medium size you asked for in stock. We hope to have delivery of these on Friday. (**4**) **As soon as** they arrive, (**5**) **I will** (**6**) **send** one out to you by first class post. Or, if (**7**) **you would prefer**, I can send you either a small or large T-shirt of the same design immediately. If this is the case, (**8**) **I would be grateful** (**9**) **if you could contact me** and let me know.
(**10**) **In the meantime**, I will try to get the medium size in as soon as possible.
(**11**) **My apologies** once again.
(**12**) **Yours sincerely**
Gareth Evans

3
1	consequently	2	nevertheless
3	In the meantime	4	Moreover
5	Following	6	However
7	Besides	8	Since

3.3
Listening Test: Part One

1 1 A year or date, eg *1996*
2 Qualities / skills, eg *presentation skills*
3 An adverb, eg *well, badly*
4 A period, eg *3 weeks*
5 An adjective, eg *confident, relaxed*
6 A verb phrase, eg *feel relaxed / listen*
7 Qualities, eg *natural abilities*
8 A plural noun, eg *meetings / business relationships*
9 A plural noun, eg *people / situations*
10 An adjective, eg *uncomfortable*
11 A training tool, eg *simulations*
12 Type of literature, eg *leaflet, brochure*

2 1 False 2 False 3 True 4 True 5 False

MODULE 4

4.1
The art of selling

1
1 H emotional benefits
2 G buying signal
3 J unique selling point
4 F payment terms
5 E sales technique
6 B competitive advantage
7 K price competition
8 A decision maker
9 I added value
10 D after-sales service

2
1 word of mouth
2 sponsorship
3 point of sale promotion
4 billboards
5 direct mail (or mailing)
6 viral marketing

3
1 C pushing   2 A buying   3 C close
4 B persuade   5 C need   6 B strategy

4
1 launched   2 have collected
3 have circulated   4 has been
5 will have decided   6 tend
7 is looking   8 will write

5
1 Up to now   2 In the last decade
3 Sooner or later   4 Currently
5 In the past   6 since I was born

6
1 Correct
2 Incorrect (*raised everyone's hopes*)
3 Correct
4 Incorrect (*has declined*)
5 Correct
6 Correct
7 Incorrect (*raise, increase,* etc)
8 Incorrect (*reducing the price*)

7
1 placing   2 delivery   3 stock
4 commission   5 mark   6 volume
7 chain   8 promotional

8
increased /t/	changed /d/
picked /t/	ended /id/
plummeted /id/	reached /t/
recovered /d/	decreased /t/
fluctuated /id/	rocketed /id/
stayed /d/	levelled /d/
developed /t/	recorded /id/
dropped /t/	

9
1 fluctuated wildly
2 reached a peak
3 continued on an upward trend with some fluctuations
4 remained relatively stable
5 recovered slightly
6 increased steadily
7 developed in a similar way
8 diverged significantly

4.2
Presenting figures

1
1 at   2 in   3 from   4 In / By
5 to   6 of   7 with   8 into / to
9 by   10 At

2
1 I'm going to present
2 If we look at the first graph
3 As you can see
4 The second graph shows
5 Comparing the two
6 In conclusion
7 Thanks for your attention
8 Now if there are any questions

3
1 It resulted **in a lot of people cancelling their holidays.**
2 It led **to a lot of people cancelling their holidays.**
3 It meant **that a lot of people cancelled their holidays.**
4 It was on account **of their (having) very talented software designers.**
5 It was thanks **to some very talented software designers.**
6 It had a lot to do **with their (having) very talented software designers.**

4.3
Writing Test: Part One

1
0 **True** – use the rubric to help you write a brief introduction to what you are going to describe.
1 **False** – some will be unavoidable, but try to rephrase the question in your own words.
2 **True**
3 **False** – just describe the general development.
4 **True** – this can either be a general comment at the beginning or conclusion at the end.
5 **False** – you only need to comment on the facts presented; if reasons are obvious then you can give them.
6 **False** – you must show that you have understood the information presented.

2 Model answer:

The graph shows the production levels achieved by factories in three different locations over the period 2000 to 2005. Overall, we can see that, although the three factories vary in size and production capacity, the output at all the sites has followed a similar upward trend.

In Guangzhou, the largest of the three, output rose from 7.6 million to 12 million units over the period in question, the best growth in percentage terms. In Timisoara, production rose by about 35% over the same period, despite a slight fall recorded in 2002. In Leeds, output also grew year on year but increased more slowly, from 7 million in 2000 to 8.5 million in 2005.

In conclusion we can observe that production at all three sites has shown a healthy level of growth, reflecting an increased demand for the company's products.

MODULE 5

5.1

Money and finance

1 1 borrowed   2 wasted   3 made   4 make
   5 charge   6 saved   7 is worth   8 spent
   9 owe   10 off

2 **lend, owe, invoice, charge** someone money <u>for</u> something
   spend, bet, save, waste money <u>on</u> something

3 1 take   2 in   3 much   4 on
   5 turnover   6 made   7 security   8 worth
   9 owe   10 accounts

5 1 than   2 much   3 by   4 as, as
   5 more   6 less

6

Adjective (or adverb)	Comparative form	Superlative form
clever	cleverer	the cleverest
good	**better**	the best
quickly	**more quickly***	**the most quickly**
tiring	**more tiring**	the most tiring
bad	worse	**the worst**
well (adverb)	**better**	**the best**
far	**further / farther**	**the furthest / the farthest**
little	**less**	the least
much	more	**the most**

* You will sometimes hear people say '*she works quicker than him*' or '*he ran the quickest of all of them*'.

7 1 Life expectancy in France **is much higher than in** Russia.
   2 Russia **has a slightly bigger population than** Japan.
   3 Zimbabwe **has a very similar number of internet users to** Syria.
   4 The number of Internet users in Mexico **is much lower than in** France.
   5 Mexico's GDP **is not nearly as high as** the USA's.
   6 China and France **have exactly the same rate of** inflation.
   7 Japan **has very low inflation compared to the** USA.
   8 The USA **is by far the richest** country in the table.
   9 Life expectancy in Zimbabwe **is much lower than in** other countries.
   10 Japan's population **is twice as big as** France's.

8 1 liabilities   2 equity   3 loss   4 turnover
   5 costs   6 gross   7 net   8 bottom
   9 creditors   10 investments

9 1 E   2 B   3 G   4 A   5 D   6 H

10 **Possible answers:**
   material costs   administrative costs   distribution costs
   labour costs   research and development costs
   finance costs   fixed costs   direct costs   rent
   advertising expenditure   maintenance costs
   capital expenditure

5.2

Discussing options

1 **Suggested answers:**
   1 Ask for someone's opinion
      What's your view / opinion of …? or What do you think?
   2 Make a suggestion
      I would recommend doing … or We could try doing …
   3 State a preference
      For me, the best thing would be to …
   4 Agree with someone
      I agree with you.
   5 Disagree politely
      I see what you're saying, but it wouldn't it be better to …
   6 Suggest an alternative course of action
      Instead of doing …, we should …

2 1 G I think it would be better to expand slowly.
   2 B I have some reservations about entering the Chinese market.
   3 A We shouldn't rush into making a decision.
   4 I The advantage of Hungary is that it's near.
   5 H We would be better off concentrating on Europe.

6 E I think China represents the best opportunity.

7 F I suggest that we wait a year.

8 D Personally, I would go for the eastern European market.

3 **MD** I wanted to ask your advice about the rise in steel prices.

DD What do you want to know exactly?

MD Well, what do you suggest that we do about it?

DD As I see it, we've got two options. We could absorb the cost or pass it on to our customers.

MD And which of those two do you recommend?

DD I'd recommend absorbing the cost for now. The price of steel may come down again.

MD My only reservation about that is that it will hurt our profit margins.

DD Maybe, in the short term, but if we were to pass the cost on, we might lose customers.

MD I see what you're saying, but wouldn't it be better to lose a few than to be unprofitable?

DD That's the decision you have to make, but you've heard my opinion now.

5.3

Listening Test: Part Two

TASK ONE – SECTOR	TASK TWO – FINANCIAL PROBLEM
1 E education	1 F being paid late
2 B clothes retail	2 C expensive premises
3 A car repair	3 G loans to repay
4 H mail order firm	4 E high cost of advertising
5 F property / real estate	5 B investment risk

MODULE 6

6.1

Purchasing power

1 1 C   2 D   3 B   4 B   5 A   6 C   7 D   8 A   9 C
10 C

2 1 extension   2 seasonal   3 squeezing   4 raw
5 exclusive   6 pass   7 terms   8 feedback

3 1 Launches *a call for tender*, giving the *technical specifications*

2 *Bids for / tenders for* the contract

3 Evaluates the *bids / offers*; makes a shortlist

4 *Negotiates* the details

5 *Awards* the contract to a supplier

6 *Wins / loses* the contract

4 1 Any company **which wishes** to be considered must submit their bid by 20 April.

2 Bids **which have been / are submitted** after that date will not be considered.

3 Anyone **who gives** inaccurate information will be disqualified.

4 Prices **which have been / are quoted** in this initial bid will be treated as negotiable.

5 Anyone **questioning** the terms should contact our contracts office.

6 Companies **owned** by a larger group or parent company must declare this fact.

7 Suppliers **unable to** fulfil all the conditions need not apply.

8 The decision **made** on 14 May will be final.

5 1 have submitted

2 will be

3 tendered

4 did

5 have not done

6 are continuing / will continue

6 1 E   2 B   3 D   4 F   5 C

7 **Suggested answer:**

Dear Mr James

I am writing to express my deep concern and anger about the fact that your team of builders have recently left the site of our offices in Portland Street with a lot of work unfinished, saying that they had been called to another job!

As you know, we contracted your company last November to fully rewire our offices and put up new partitioning. Work began in February and seemed to be progressing well. The wiring was fitted quickly and the partitioning also went up easily.

However, the job is by no means finished. Some of the new wiring is still exposed and the partitioning is not properly secured. Both these things represent a real health and safety hazard: someone could get electrocuted or fall through a wall. The consequence is that I have had to order some of the staff to work from home, while the remainder are squeezed into a small space not affected by your work.

This situation is not tolerable. It is costing our company valuable time and money. Unless your team return immediately, I will be forced to employ another building firm to come in and finish the job that you started. Their fees will be charged to you, or rather, will be deducted from your invoice, when it arrives.

I am sorry to give such an ultimatum, but the circumstances leave me no other choice. I look forward to hearing from you very soon.

Yours sincerely,

8 1 <u>w</u>ork w<u>a</u>lk l<u>ear</u>n

Both contain the sound /ɜː/ as in *were*; *walk* has the sound /ɔː/ as in *door*

2 l<u>a</u>wyer l<u>au</u>nch l<u>a</u>w

Both contain the sound /ɔː/ as in *door*; *lawyer* has the sound /ɔɪ/ as in *boy*

3 sp<u>e</u>cial legal pr<u>e</u>sent

Both contain the sound /e/; *legal* has the sound /iː/ as in *keep*

4 <u>a</u>gent f<u>ai</u>lure chat

Both contain the sound /eɪ/ as in *say*; *chat* has the sound /æ/

5 m<u>o</u>nth h<u>o</u>nest fr<u>o</u>nt

Both contain the sound /ʌ/ as in *cup*; *honest* has the sound /ɒ/ as in *hot*

6.2
Telephoning

1 1 F 2 D 3 B 4 G 5 A 6 C

2 **Suggested answers:**

1 His line is engaged. Would you like to hold?

No, that's OK. I'll **call back later**.

2 Can I give you the address?

Sure. One minute, I'll **just get a pen**.

3 Can I speak to someone in technical support?

One moment, I'll **put you through**.

4 Is the correct figure 7.8 or 8.7?

Hang on, I'll **check**.

5 I need the information urgently.

OK. I'll **send it to you immediately**.

6 Please tell Kevin that I will meet him outside 210 Regent Street at 10.30.

OK. I'll **give him the message**.

7 Do you have the information to hand?

No, but I'll **get back to you as soon as I can**.

8 So, 6 o'clock tomorrow at the Red Lion pub in George Street.

Great. I'll **look forward to it / seeing you then**.

3 **Suggested answers:**

1 Hang on, please. I'll see if he's free.

2 Can I tell him who's calling?

3 Thank you, Mrs Jordan. I'll just put you through.

4 Hello. Fernandez speaking. How can I help you?

5 I'm from Mcmillion Publishers. I'm just calling to ask if you can make it to the talk this evening.

6 I'll just check my diary. I'm afraid I'm already busy this evening.

7 Don't worry. It'll be repeated on 12 May. Does that suit you any better?

8 Perhaps. I'll have to get back to you on that.

9 OK. I'll look forward to hearing from you.

6.3
Writing Test: Part Two

1 Register: B

Tone: B

Content: C

2 1 experienced 2 As 3 result
4 order 5 willing / happy 6 hearing
7 from 8 sincerely

3 **Model answer:**

Dear Mr Opik

I apologise for missing your recent call concerning your new pool. I was also sorry and surprised to hear that you have experienced problems with it so soon.

As you will recall, when we originally discussed the question of heaters, I presented to you various options. Some were smaller heaters, others were more powerful. Clearly, different people have different tastes in how warm they would like their swimming pool to be. Consequently, at the time, I advised you to buy one that you thought would be best for you. You chose a smaller, less expensive one. I am sorry that you are now regretting that choice. As a result of this, we feel that it is not our responsibility to compensate you for a new heater.

However, I do sympathise with your situation and in order to resolve this problem, I suggest that you ask the manufacturer for an exchange for a bigger heater. Generally, they are quite good about this sort of thing and should give you a full refund on the original heater.

If you like, I would be very willing to come and give my advice on which heater I personally would put in. This visit and advice would be free of charge.

I hope you find this solution acceptable and look forward to hearing from you.

Yours sincerely.

Selma Chakrabati

MODULE 7

7.1
Managing people

1 1 B 2 A 3 G 4 D 5 I 6 J 7 C 8 K 9 F 10 H

2 1 get <u>my</u> hands dirty

2 get on with

3 <u>puts</u> people on the spot

4 <u>spreads</u> <u>himself</u> very thin

5 take <u>that</u> on board

6 cut corners

7 bite off more than you can chew

8 open a can of worms

3
1 different: /kæn/ /kɑːnt/
2 same: /bɔːd/
3 different: /fɜːst/ /fɑːst/
4 different: /liːd/ /laɪd/
5 same: /piːs/
6 same: /weɪt/
7 different: /wɒnt/ /wəʊnt/

4
1 Actually, I did an MBA **to avoid having** to look for a job immediately.
2 My main motivation was **just to understand** business better.
3 I wanted to do an MBA **in order to meet** people from different backgrounds.
4 I waited until I was 33 to do my MBA **so that I could get** the maximum benefit from it.
5 I did the MBA just **in case it was** useful in later life.
6 I was sent on an MBA by my insecure boss **to prevent me from taking** over his job!

5 **Suggested answers:**
1 I am going to **read a lot more** to expand my vocabulary.
2 I am going to **listen to native speakers whenever possible** in order to improve my pronunciation.
3 I am going to **get some interview coaching** in case I am asked to speak English at a job interview.
4 I am going to make a list of my most common mistakes to avoid **making the same mistakes again and again.**
5 I am going to read more business magazines in order **to increase my knowledge of business matters.**
6 I am going to watch more English TV so that **I can understand fast native speech better.**

6
1 She rarely keeps anyone waiting.
2 He performs best under pressure.
3 He is never at his desk.
4 If you want something done properly, do it yourself.
5 I was completely exhausted after the trip.
6 Please send me an update at this address every Monday.
7 They will move their headquarters to Shanghai next month.

7
1 *Nearly half reckon firing up to 5% a year would be a good thing.*
2 *The findings suggest many managers aren't doing enough to keep their staff interested, …*
3 *… active disengagement … employees … going sick, not trying, leaving, or threatening strikes.*
4 *… bottom-slicing the 'worst' employees'*
5 *… teams with the most talented individuals don't always win.*
6 *… forced ranking introduces fear and competition, …*
7 *… getting outstanding performance from 'ordinary' resources …*

8 1 A 2 C 3 D 4 A 5 C 6 D 7 B

7.2
Report writing

1 *All these points are important, but if you fail to observe those marked ++ you risk not passing this part of the exam.*

Answer all the points you have been asked to address accurately. ++

Begin with a clear introduction of the aims of the report. +

End with a definite conclusion and recommendation. ++

Use sub-headings and bullet points to make the report clearer. +

Be consistent in your arguments and connect your ideas with linking expressions. ++

Use language naturally, appropriately and with a minimum of errors. ++

Use sophisticated vocabulary and grammatical structure. +

Organise the report so that it is clear which point is being addressed. ++

2
0	to present	'The aim is' + infinitive
1	choice	Verb 'to choose'; noun 'a choice'
2	initial	Adjective needed to describe the noun
3	most	Superlative, 'more' is used when comparing two things
4	at	at a cost
5	powerful	The suffix 'ful' has a single 'l'
6	a	it is one of many bargains
7	to get	'It is difficult' + infinitive
8	Another	'The other' or 'another'; never 'the another'
9	All	'Every' is singular, 'all' is plural
10	guarantees	Spelling
11	which	'that' is only used in defining relative clauses, eg 'the car that I rented.'
12	purchasing	'recommend' + gerund
13	no	'It has no …' or 'It doesn't have any …'
14	could	could = might = perhaps it will be; 'can' cannot be used to speculate in this way
15	in	in the long run.

3
1 Although   2 On the whole   3 However
4 since   5 Indeed

7.3
Reading Test: Part Two

1 1 D 2 F 3 H 4 B 5 E 6 A

MODULE 8

8.1
Being responsible

1
1 Another letter to the newspaper about the waste of energy in hotels.
2 For having refrigerators and freezers which are open, so needing more energy to keep food cold.
3 It is much too cheap for people to be conscious of the need to save it.
4 We are not a society that values saving money.
5 We will soon reach a turning point where companies are forced to be more energy-conscious.

2
1 The hotel industry is just the tip of the iceberg = *He is obviously right but why single out the hotel industry?*
2 People who take no notice = *indifferent passers-by*
3 Consumers should vote with their feet = *Stop spending money with organisations that accept or even encourage waste*

3 **Suggested answers:**
Waste: They can use less packaging, especially plastic containers and wrapping.
Transport: They can use lorries / trucks that run on greener fuel.
They can try to minimise the distance between warehouses and stores.
Energy: They can switch off the lights at night if they are not needed.
They can use freezers and refrigerators that have doors.
They can buy green energy or install generation facilities onsite, like wind turbines or solar panels.
Suppliers: They can trade more with fair trade suppliers.
They can buy more local produce in order to reduce food miles.

4
1 smog
2 extinction
3 drought
4 leak
5 flooding

5
1 Uromin shares increased **by** $1.2 **over** the six-month period.
2 Formetal shares stayed **at** the same level **for** three months.
3 **On** average both shares showed a rise **of** 50%.
4 Formetal shares climbed **to** $5.4 **by** the end of June.
5 Uromin shares reached a peak **of** $3.7 **in** May.

6
1 asking
2 to change
3 to establish
4 worrying
5 taking
6 to have
7 paying
8 beginning

7 to be committed / to get used / to look forward / to object + **to** do**ing** something OR **to** something

8 **Suggested answers:**
1 You should knock before entering.
2 You mustn't take photographs in the main hall.
3 You must be authorised to enter this area.
4 You don't have to present a badge if you are a member of staff / you must present a badge unless you are a member of staff.
5 You should register here.
6 You may help yourself to (take) a catalogue.

9
1 F being accountable to the outside world for your actions
2 I considering the welfare of your employees
3 G taking account of the impact of your actions
4 H embracing the challenge of doing business in a sustainable way
5 B taking responsibility for your environment
6 A playing a part in fighting poverty, unemployment and social injustice
7 C being committed to growing your business by ethical means
8 E being prepared to disclose information

10 1 is   2 that   3 by   4 This   5 also   6 the

11

Adjective	Noun
accountable	accountability
sustainable	**sustainability**
unjust	injustice
poor	**poverty**
environmental	environment
committed	**commitment**
involved	**involvement**
respectful (or **respected**)	respect
beneficial	benefit
honest	**honesty**
considerate	consideration

12 The general rule for words of three syllables or more is that the stress falls on the third syllable from the end, except:
with nouns that end -*tion*, and adjectives that end -*ic*, when the stress falls on the syllable before the final syllable;
with nouns that end -*ment*, where the stress falls in the same place as the verb they are derived from.

sus**tain**able	sustaina**bil**ity
un**just**	in**jus**tice
p**oor**	**pov**erty
environ**men**tal	en**vi**ronment
com**mit**ted	com**mit**ment
in**vol**ved	in**vol**vement
res**pect**ful	res**pect**
bene**fi**cial	**be**nefit
honest	**hon**esty
con**sid**erate	conside**ra**tion

8.2
Formal meetings

1 **Suggested answers:**

1 What's on the agenda?
2 Could I just interrupt?
3 Sorry, could I just finish?
4 Can we move on?
5 I think we should take a break / adjourn for coffee.
6 Perhaps we can come back to this later.
7 That's a very good point.
8 We're running a little short of time.
9 I think John is better placed to answer that.
10 OK Let's leave it there. / I think we should stop there. To sum up, …

2
1 If I could just interrupt
2 could I just finish
3 That's a good point
4 we should move on to the next item on the agenda
5 I think Kate is better placed to answer that
6 If I understand you correctly

8.3
Reading Test: Part Four

1 1 A 2 B 3 C 4 C 5 B 6 D 7 A 8 A 9 D 10 B

MODULE 9
9.1
Innovation

1
1 Space Saving Kitchens — **neat and compact solutions**
2 Rioch Architects — **innovative state-of-the-art designs**
3 Presto Printing — **fast and efficient service**
4 TQ Clothing Company — **up-market designer labels at low prices**
5 Bettaprice Foods — **unbeatable value for money**
6 Durawork Power Tools — **reliable quality equipment**

2
1	compact	**bulky**
2	modern	**old-fashioned**
3	up-market	**down-market**
4	value for money	**overpriced**
5	reliable	**unreliable / erratic**
6	efficient	**inefficient**

3

/ɑɪ/	/ɪ/
reliable	equipment
private	image
finance	finish
realise	negative
client	limited
silent	efficient
	simple
	quality

4 1 at / in 2 of 3 in 4 at 5 to 6 on 7 with 8 with

5

at	in	on
the same time	the world	a small scale
home	the market*	the market*
the end of the day	the pipeline	holiday
least	the end	the face of it
	the future	average
	practice	

* *on the market* means 'available to buy', *in the market for* means you want to buy something.

6 **Suggested answers:**
1 In principle, **that would be** no problem.
2 If you could deliver direct, **it would be** easier for us.
3 **I would accept** your invitation, but I'm afraid I have another appointment.
4 **I would appreciate** your help, because I don't think I can do it on my own.
5 If I were in your shoes, **I would do** the same.
6 Before agreeing anything, **we would need** certain guarantees from you.

7
1 Would you be prepared / willing to give us a discount?
2 I would need to discuss that with my boss.
3 That would be convenient for us too.
4 That would be difficult for us.
5 We would be happy to accept those terms.
6 In exchange, would you be able to guarantee that …

8
1 out of   2 up with   3 out for
4 up with   5 forward to   6 up to

9 1 The *competition* is general (=*all the competitors together*), a *competitor* is single and specific.

2 *Differentiate* is to make something be or appear different; *make a difference* is to make a contribution or have a noticeable effect

3 *Efficiency* is to do with saving time, money and effort; *effectiveness* is getting results.

4 When you are behind you have to *catch up* (*reach the same level*), then you have to *keep up* (=*stay at the same level*); finally, you *get ahead of the competition.*

5 You try to *retain* good employees (=*keep hold of*); you try to *sustain* an advantage (=*keep up*).

6 A *patent* gives the copyright or intellectual ownership of an idea; a *licence* is a permission to do or sell something.

10 1 innovative   2 followers   3 growth
4 spending   5 failures   6 driver
7 existing

9.2
Negotiating

1 1 Doesn't say: it does say that fewer women than men like the win-lose approach.

2 True ... *when a high degree of concern is expressed for the substance ...*

3 True

4 False ... *they place ... relationships above the fairness of the outcome ...*

5 True ... *yielding to pressure to preserve the relationship ...*

2 1 D 2 H 3 B 4 G 5 C 6 A 7 F 8 E

3 1 F 2 H 3 C 4 G 5 D 6 E 7 A

9.3
Reading and Listening Tests: Part Three

1 1 A *Europe's car industry is endangering its main selling point by being reluctant to commit money early enough to new technological innovations*

2 C *The risk for suppliers is higher and the payback time is longer*

3 C *because Bosch is known for being extremely careful in its public statements*

4 B *that if it was a company listed on the stock market, it may not have accepted the initial high losses when developing diesel pumps*

5 D *suppliers and manufacturers should decide on standards for new technologies much earlier to avoid costly competition*

6 D *with some growth in Europe, a decline in the US and booming business in India and China.*

MODULE 10
10.1
Travel and entertainment

1 1 Amy   2 Amy   3 Amy   4 Tony   5 Tony   6 Tony
7 Amy   8 Tony

2 A Ummmm ... I think I'll have the steak.
A is looking at the menu and deciding now (spontaneous decision)

B I'm going to have the lobster.
B has looked at the menu and already decided (plan or intention)

C I'm just having some soup
C has already ordered soup and is now waiting for it to arrive (arrangement)

3 *The present simple is used for schedules and timetables.*
The present continuous is used for arrangements.
'going to' is used for things decided and also for confident predictions.
'will' is used for general predictions, spontaneous decisions or offers and simple statement of fact.

1 is
2 are meeting
3 are you going to say
4 am going to tell / will tell
5 gives
6 will have
7 won't like / is not going to like
8 is happening
9 are hosting
10 will be / is going to be
11 will be / are
12 does / will it end
13 will bring / is bringing
14 am going to try

4 1
1 publicity   2 venue   3 reflect
4 put on   5 award
2
1 get   2 ice   3 treat
4 estimate   5 turn up

5 **go** missing / crazy / bankrupt / to plan / over budget / quiet / shopping
get to know someone / married / lost / people involved / started / tired

6 **Suggested answers:**

A lot of things could **go wrong** if we don't prepare carefully.

I can't find the quotation I sent them. It's **gone missing**.

She's **going to go crazy** when she find out.

They **went bankrupt** because of cashflow problems.

Everything's **going** according **to plan**.

We **went** a little **over budget** but not too badly.

I am going to **go shopping** at lunchtime.

I need to **get ready** for the meeting. It starts in five minutes.

She's a really nice woman when you **get to know** her.

He **got married** when he was 21.

I'd take a taxi if I were you. It's very easy to **get lost** in the one way system.

I always try to **get people involved** when I give a talk by giving them a little exercise to do.

OK. Everyone's here. Shall we **get started**?

I am **getting** very **tired** of waiting.

7
1 The‿y‿ opening will be‿y‿a‿teigh‿tam.
2 We didn't go‿w‿ou‿to‿w‿a restaurant.
3 I‿y‿a‿minterested, if you‿w‿are.
4 Can we just go‿w‿over the‿y‿agenda?
5 Do you‿w‿ever lie‿y‿about you‿rage?

10.2
The language of proposals

1 I would like to draw your attention to the performance
Unfortunately, it has experienced some problems in the market,
The main problem is our advertising campaign, not the product. We need to find a different way to advertise the product
By contrast, they have used innovative styles of marketing and advertising,
we should design some advertisements which feel fresh and attractive and run these on different types of advertising media: TV, radio, magazines, billboards etc.
we should use some famous people in the advertisements, because this will help to persuade consumers that it is a good product

2 **Suggested answer:**

To: The directors

Following the disappointing recent performance of the energy drink, Zap, I would like to suggest some action we can take to reverse this trend.

Unfortunately, **sales have not grown at all in the last nine months**, while our competitors products have improved their sales by an average of 8%. We need to take steps urgently to deal with this situation.

The main problem is our advertising campaign. **We are still running the original TV advertisement, using the same**

characters – a number of ordinary people, in their 30s mainly, doing various sports (with the help of ZAP). We need to build a new story around the product, using new characters – perhaps well-known athletes – to advertise the product or it will continue to lose market share to its competitors.

By contrast, our competitors have focused on the youth market by sponsoring events such as the World Skateboard championships. They have also placed their energy drinks in more specialized shops, like cycling shops. In this way, they have attracted a lot of new customers. We must do the same.

My recommendations are as follows:

– to employ the some advertising specialists to help us define a new campaign.

– to create advertisements which appeal to a younger age group and use more humour. These could be run on TV but also on the Internet where young people are more likely to see them.

– to get the endorsement of an up-and-coming sporting hero, a footballer for example, that young people can really identify with.

Please consider these proposals carefully and do not hesitate to contact me for further details.

10.3
Speaking Test: Part Three

1 **Suggested answers:**
- More use of video and telephone conferencing
- Travel only to essential meetings
- Try to stay for shorter periods when abroad
- Offer a prize for staff who save the most on travel

2 **Suggested answers:**
1 What do you think about … / do you have any views on …
2 In my opinion / For me
3 The main thing / the most important issue
4 On the other hand
5 I agree with you.
6 It is also true
7 furthermore / in addition
8 Good idea.
9 just to sum up
10 've agreed

MODULE 11

11.1

The economy

1 Ordinary working people's pay has not gone up in line with company profits.

The country's debts are preventing new business ideas from being tried out.

The cost of medical treatment is too high for the middle class.

The American economy is founded on ordinary people earning money for their hard work.

2
1 cost of / standard of / ~~quality of~~ **living**
2 ~~blooming~~ / booming / buoyant **economy**
3 private / ~~civil~~ / public **sector**
4 job / labour / ~~work~~ **market**
5 **trade** ~~excess~~ / deficit / surplus
6 **tax** burden / bill / ~~load~~
7 **consumer** ~~faith~~ / confidence / spending
8 **government** ~~present~~ / subsidy / loan
9 **power** ~~consuming~~ / buying / purchasing

3 1 A 2 D 3 G 4 B 5 F 6 E

4
1 D relocate   2 B encourage
3 H depressed   4 I disabled
5 C competition   6 A confidence
7 G inefficiency   8 E unemployment

5
1 don't mind, will leave   2 was / were, would do
3 won't, is   4 would find, was / were not
5 wanted, would triple   6 would take, thought
7 will mind, borrow*

** If it was an unlikely request it would also be possible to say: 'Do you think that he **would mind** if I **borrowed** his car?'*

6 **Possible answers:**
1 If I had something very important that I needed to finish
2 If it were only a small gift
3 If the job involved a lot more stress and much longer hours
4 If I had enough money already to live out my retirement comfortably
5 If I felt I was not being taken seriously
6 If someone had made a really bad factual mistake

7 **Possible answers:**
1 more working mothers will stay in employment
2 unemployed people will be forced to find work
3 a lot of high earners will leave the country
4 it will encourage people to set up their own companies
5 it will help children to learn key computer skills
6 it will reduce the number of cars on the road

8 **Long**: laid, sleep, fo**o**d, m**o**ve, m**e**dium, include, range, client, b**o**th

Short: said, slip, g**oo**d, above, m**e**dical, p**u**dding, r**a**ng, clinic, cl**o**th

10
1 outgoing   2 premises   3 rental
4 grants   5 estate   6 property
7 move   8 exempt

11 1 A 2 E 3 B 4 H 5 D 6 I 7 C 8 F

12 1 on 2 in 3 for 4 to 5 out 6 about
7 out, for 8 in 9 on

11.2

Effective writing

1
1 First of all
2 For example
3 Unfortunately
4 Moreover
5 So
6 As I see it
7 On the one hand
8 Although

2 **Suggested answers:**
1 We consider that $150 is too expensive for a top of the range hairdryer.
2 To sum up, my preference would be the second option, since it is important to find a more cost-effective solution.

3 **Suggested answers:**

Dear Jim

I hope you are well. (**0**) I'm sorry about the long delay in replying to your email, (**1**) **but** I wanted to research your question thoroughly before (**2**) **replying.**

You (**3**) **asked if** it was possible to extend the life of our standard mobile phone battery, (**4**) **because** you have received a (**5**) **lot** of complaints about it. The answer is 'yes', but the solution may be expensive. We source our batteries from a Korean supplier which manufactures three different grades of battery. The ones (**6**) **we buy** are the cheapest in the range. (**7**) **Not surprisingly**, they also have the shortest life.

If you (**8**) **want** me to send you more technical details, (**9**) **feel free to** ask me.

11.3
Speaking Test: Part Two

1
1 find
2 making
3 have
4 on
5 easy
6 I have mentioned
7 to prioritise
8 would like to
9 make
10 to do
11 should
12 to
13 you can even have

2 Suggested answers:
- In what kind of jobs is it important to be able to manage your time?
- With modern communications, is it easier or more difficult for business people to manage their time nowadays?

MODULE 12

12.1
Crossing cultures

1 Suggested answers:
1 *global* village
2 multinational *corporations*
3 *trade* barriers
4 cheap *imports / goods*
5 *free* movement of capital
6 global *economy / market / trade*
7 *developed/ developing / under-developed* countries
8 deregulated *market / economy*

2
1 John J Sweeney
2 Paul Samuelson
3 William Greider
4 Jack Welch
5 Frederic Jameson
6 Robert Reich

3 *wish* + past perfect
should + *have* + past participle
If + past perfect, *would* + *have* + past participle
Could / might + *have* + past participle
Suggested answers:
I **wish** they **hadn't sold** the business.
We **should have researched** the market more thoroughly.
If she **hadn't attended** the conference, she **wouldn't have missed** the deadline.
I **might have changed** my mind if I had read the report.

4
It must have been …   99% yes
It could have been …   50%
It may have been …   50%
It might have been …   50%
It can't have been …   99% no
(*Could* is sometimes used for situations which seem less likely than *might* and *may*.)

5
1 If I **had felt** more confident, I would have taken the risk.
2 You should **have asked** me. I would have said 'yes'.
3 If you had lost it, I **would have been** furious.
4 I wish that I **hadn't mentioned** that I was looking for another job.
5 I don't know why he's so late. I suppose he might **have forgotten**.
6 I don't think anyone could **have predicted** that this would happen.

6
1 They wished they had done more tests before launching the new product.
2 They could have got a better response if they had advertised externally.
3 He should have consulted more people.
4 She wished that she had gone to university.
5 If she kept her shares, she would have lost a lot of money.
6 If either side had made a compromise, they might have reached an agreement.
7 I should have taken the job.
8 They could avoided bankruptcy if they had invested more.

7 Normally a 'g' is hard if followed by the vowels a, o, u and soft if followed by e or i. But there are exceptions!
Hard: target, colleague, angle, guest, legal, global
Soft: merge, manager, gentleman, angel, gesture, region, margin

8
1 casually OR formally
2 shake hands OR nod your head
3 by his formal title OR by his first name
4 exchanging small talk OR chatting OR getting to know him / her

9 **The ultimate gesture = the smile**

10
1 nod
2 common
3 contact
4 feature
5 losing
6 rude
7 greet
8 hand
9 awareness

12.2
Social English

1 1 H 2 D 3 I 4 F 5 G 6 C 7 E 8 A

2 Suggested answers:

1 Pleased to meet you, Jane.

2 Don't worry. I'm not in a hurry.

3 Not at all. / You're very welcome.

4 Yes, it is.

5 Not bad, thanks.

6 That's very kind of you but I can manage.

7 Thank you. So are you.

8 That would be great.

9 Please. Go ahead.

10 No, go ahead / Actually, I'd rather you didn't.

3 1 well   2 to hear   3 would be   4 out   5 worry
6 go ahead   7 in   8 so   9 it   10 of

12.3
Reading Test: Part Five and Part Six

1 1 its   2 of   3 even   4 with   5 not   6 had   7 is
8 than   9 at   10 then

2

1 correct	2 can	3 correct
4 with	5 not	6 correct
7 more	8 correct	9 on
10 been	11 correct	12 that